IN THE

SHADOW

OF THE

ROCKIES

OTHER BOOKS BY ROBERT J. ADAMS

* * *

THE STUMP FARM

BEYOND THE STUMP FARM

HORSE COP

FISH COP

THE ELEPHANT'S TRUNK

THE SOUTH ROAD

SKUNKS AND HOUND DOGS

DYNAMITE HILL

IN THE
SHADOW
OF THE
ROCKIES

ROBERT J. ADAMS

MEGAMY

THE PUBLISHER:
Megamy Publishing Ltd.
P. O. Box 3507
Spruce Grove, Alberta, Canada T7X 3A7
E-mail: megamy@compusmart.ab.ca

National Library of Canada Cataloguing in Publication
Adams, Robert J., 1938–
    In the shadow of the Rockies/Robert J. Adams

ISBN 0-9733728-0-X

    1. Adams, Robert J., 1938– 2. Game Wardens--Rocky
Mountains, Canadian(B.C. and Alta.)--Anecdotes.
  3. Outdoor life--Rocky Mountains, Canadian(B.C. and Alta.)--
Anecdotes. I. Title.

SK354.A33A3 2003   *639.9'092*   *C2003-904556-0*

Senior Editor: Kelly Hymanyk
Copy Editor: Natalie King
Design, layout, and production: Kelly Hymanyk
Cover: NEXUS Design
Printing: Blitzprint

DEDICATION

To my son-in-law, Bill

DISCLAIMER

The stories you are about to read are all true. The men, women, and children you will read about are all people from my past. I have taken the liberty of changing the names of many of them to protect their identities. Although I view the past as being very humorous, they may not.

CONTENTS

Acknowledgements

Introduction

ACKNOWLEDGEMENTS

I would like to thank Mar for her contribution to this book. Who could have imagined the nightmare she faced when I accepted the posting to Hinton. The first year in my dream district would have challenged the patience of Job.

I have a special thanks to Natalie King for the great job of copy-editing. And to Greg Dussome for our cover design.

Once again, the credit for this book must go to my daughter Kelly. I can only thank you for believing in your father.

Thank you, all.

INTRODUCTION

Robert J. Adams has mastered the art of "laughing at yourself". His ability to find humour in situations that could otherwise be stressful or aggravating or embarrassing is what endears him to us. We root for him as he struggles with the Powers That Be. We laugh with him, we cheer him on. His obstacles are our obstacles.

Adams is once again successful in sharing his journey with his readers, allowing them to relive memorable moments of their own and laugh through him.

MEGAMY PURBLISHING

IN THE

SHADOW

OF THE

ROCKIES

AH YES, IT IS
A BRAND-NEW OFFICE!

I stared at the memo, hardly able to believe my eyes. Not only had I asked for a transfer to the newly created Fish and Wildlife District, but I had actually got it. And I was holding the proof in my hot, unbelieving hand.

"Yes!" I yelled. "I got the plum! A mountain district! I'm going to Hinton!"

I was a pretty excited young man. To think that I had actually got something that I had asked for, and a mountain district at that. There had been no need to sell me on Hinton—why, it was practically in my own backyard, only 45 miles from Edson. Baby, I was going home.

"Start packing," I sang out to Mar as I burst through the door. I was on such a high, I hadn't even bothered to say hello.

"What do you mean, start packing? Where are we

going?" she asked. Obviously Mar had forgotten about my request for a transfer, or . . . or maybe she had heard so many of my requests for transfer that she had stopped listening.

"Hinton!" I trumpeted triumphantly. "I applied for Hinton, and would you believe I got it! We're going to Hinton!"

"You gotta be kidding me," she replied in a voice that was barely audible. I could tell by the sound of her voice and the look on her face that she was surprised.

"No siree," I chortled happily. "Lookee here, Mar, it says so right here in this memo. Start packing, we're on our way to the mountains!"

"You mean you really got it? You got what you asked for?" she said, sounding sad. "When you said you were going to apply for Hinton, I didn't think you were really serious."

"You bet I was serious," I crowed.

"When do we have to go?"

"The sooner the better," I bubbled happily. I could hardly wait. "Actually, April 15th is the official date, but we should drive up as soon as possible and look for a house. Maybe we should go up this weekend."

"Don't you think you're rushing it a little?" Mar asked.

She didn't seem to be quite as happy about this transfer as I was. I couldn't understand it. It wasn't as though we owned a house we had to sell; we were renting, so we were free to move with only a month's notice. We could easily find a house in Hinton. I knew that Mar had to quit her job, and she was making more money than I, but that little situation was no different from when we had left Brooks. There would be jobs in Hinton; there were always jobs, she could get another job there. She would be leaving all her friends; but then, she hadn't known anybody in Strathmore when we transferred there. There would be more friends in Hinton. Maybe it was the prairies. After all, Mar was a prairie girl, a stubble-jumper from Saskatchewan — maybe she'll miss the prairies. Yes, that had to be it, the thought of leaving all the wide open spaces for the friendly confines of the magnificent Alberta Rockies, being surrounded by trees, looking up to the skies to see the tops of the mountains was probably more excitement than she could handle.

"And I suppose they told you there was a brand-new office in Hinton," she said rather sarcastically.

"Why, yes. As a matter of fact, they did."

"Just like there was supposed to be a brand-new office in Strathmore when we moved here. Well, I can tell you one thing right now, you won't be using my house as an office this time. You can just tell the government that my house belongs to me and not them. I won't tolerate . . ." and on and on Mar droned, while my thoughts wandered back to my last phone call with the Powers That Be.

"That's right, Adams, there is a brand-new office in Hinton. I was in Hinton last week and I checked it out myself. In fact, it's so new that not a single soul has ever set foot in it since it was built," said one of the Powers That Be, giving me his assurance. But I knew there was no sense mentioning that conversation with Mar; there had been too many promises before.

"Right, Mar," I replied, once more tuning in on her concerns. "I swear I'll tell them. There's no way they're using your house for an office on this transfer. That's a promise."

Yes, transfers were always traumatic times, but they were a fact of life, the life we had chosen, the life of a District Fish and Wildlife officer. Oh yeah, we were headed for Hinton. For me, it was homecoming time; for Mar, it was another faceless town full of strangers. I figured I had gotten the ultimate plum; Mar figured she had gotten the proverbial shaft.

It was late March when we finally took our house hunting trip.

"You're gonna love Hinton," I said, as I stole a look at the unhappy person sitting beside me in the car. We had dropped our daughters, Kelly and Robin, at my parents' place in Edson before starting on the last leg of our journey. I could barely contain myself as we drove west on Highway 16 towards Hinton. We had just started through the Obed Hills when we were greeted by the first signs of Hinton.

"What's that stink?" Mar snorted. She wrinkled up her nose and gave me the most disgusted look one person could ever give another.

"Hold your shirt, Mar," I quickly replied. "That's not me. That's the pulp mill. You know, I've heard some of the locals say that is the smell of money."

"It doesn't smell like any money I've ever smelled," she declared, then snorted and shook her head, trying to get the smell out of her nostrils. Suddenly she gagged and her whole body retched.

"You'll be okay," I replied sympathetically. "You'll get used to it in no time."

"No, I won't get used to it," she said, and gave me a dagger stare as she gagged again. "That's it! I've had enough of Hinton! You can turn this car around, right now. Let's go back. I want to go home before I get real sick."

Mar gagged and complained, and her health seemed to deteriorate the closer we got to Hinton. I felt sorry for her. I remembered my first meeting with the Hinton stench.

I was playing baseball in Hinton as a young man. The odour was always there, and on cloudy, humid days I can still see the thick green smog belching from the mill. Like a sheet — no, like a thick, heavy blanket — it poured like tar from the smokestack and plummeted to the ground. I watched the green mass roll across the road, across the field, before engulfing the baseball diamond. Being the centre fielder, I was the first to receive the goods. The whole place took on a pukey green colour. I swear that stuff was thick enough that I could have taken a knife and cut a chunk right out of it.

"Relax, Mar, you'll be fine," I said, trying to reassure her. "It just takes a little getting used to. We'll just pop into town, find us a house to rent, check out the brand-new office, and be out of here. We'll be back in Edson before you know it."

"I don't want to go to Edson. I don't want to go to Hinton. I want to go home," she wailed. "I don't feel good. I'm gonna be sick and I just want to go home."

"You're probably just hungry," I said. "What do you say — let's get a bite to eat before we go house hunting."

For our dining pleasure, we chose to eat in our car at a drive-in. Perhaps eating was the wrong suggestion.

"The milk's sour!" she complained as she took the first sip. She barely had time to get the car door open before she vomited. The smell from the mill was really doing a number on Mar, and her condition did not improve as we drove from place to place inquiring about lodging for our little family.

Hinton was a booming town in 1966. To the north, McIntyre Porcupine was opening a coal mine, and a new townsite was being developed at Grande Cache. A new railway was being built between Hinton and Grande Cache, and numerous construction companies were running their operations from Hinton. South of town, Cardinal River Coal was establishing a new mine on the site of the old Luscar Collieries. They too were basing their operations out of Hinton. And of course, highways were being built or upgraded in both directions.

Hinton was a beehive of activity, bursting at the seams. The influx of so many people and the resulting activity were causing many growing pains. The little town was struggling to satisfy the demands of the booming economy. Much to our surprise and my chagrin, we soon found out that there was no accommodation available. There was not a house for rent or for sale. There was not a suite or room to be found. Hotels were booked solid. In short, there was no room at the inn. To make matters worse, not a single soul that I talked to had heard of the brand-new Fish and Wildlife Office that was hidden in some obscure place in town. Reluctantly, I had to admit that moving into Hinton was not going to be as easy as I had anticipated.

Mar's condition did not improve as we drove east, leaving Hinton and the stench from the mill behind. At Edson I checked her into the hospital. There she received an emergency appendectomy. I returned to Strathmore alone.

"How was Hinton?" asked the Powers That Be.

"You don't want to know," I replied, and shook my head unhappily.

"Now, tell me, what could be wrong?" asked the Powers That Be.

"Everything!" I snorted in disgust. "Hinton is no different than Strathmore was when you sent me there. There's not a house or a room in the whole place for sale or rent. I even went to the town hall and inquired about a lot. Would you believe there's not even a lot for sale! And nobody seems to have heard about that brand-new office you promised me."

"Did you talk to the manager at the Hinton Hotel?"

"I did, and he assured me that the only way I was going to get a room was to buy the hotel, and it wasn't for sale," I said.

"No, no, Adams, did you ask him about your office?"

"No . . ." I replied, and hesitated before adding,

"Why would I ask the hotel manager about my office? He rents rooms, not offices."

"You see, Adams, you have to ask all the questions if you want all the answers. You go back and ask him. He'll show you your office. It's right behind the hotel."

As the moving day dawned, it was decision time, time to bite the bullet. I had contacted everybody I knew in Hinton, but had failed to find any housing. Martha and our two young daughters travelled to Saskatchewan and stayed with her parents. I went to Hinton. Just as the Powers That Be had told me, there was a brand-new office and it was right behind the Hinton Hotel.

A huge empty room complete with nothing except a large storage room — ah, that would be my personal office — and a fully functional bathroom. It took me no time at all to dress it up with furnishings within my allotted budget: fruit crates. Yes, I furnished my entire office in the rustic style of grocery store discards. I was proud of my decorating abilities. Jack, the hotel manager, did not share my enthusiasm.

"Enter, my friend," I called out to Jack when he paid me a visit. He stood in the doorway staring in disbelief. "And please, close the door. Oh, and your mouth too; you're letting the flies in."

"I-I saw your car and I thought I'd . . . just drop in and say hello . . . a-and what in blue blazes is this?" he stammered as he surveyed the room.

"What is this, you ask? Why, my friend, you are looking at the brand-new Hinton Fish and Wildlife Office, complete with the latest decor," I replied, waving my arms out and around to make sure that he didn't miss a single item.

"You're pulling my leg, aren't you?" he said. Jack appeared to be having a wee bit of difficulty coming to grips with my interior decorating skills.

"So, what do you think of my office furnishings? It's what you might call your basic early settler, rustic pine box style, by R.J.A."

"Now I've seen everything," he sputtered as he walked over and looked at my desk (two wooden apple crates), my chair (one wooden apple crate), and my filing cabinet, the showpiece of the entire office — an orange crate.

"Pretty good, eh? Bet you didn't think I could get this place in shape this fast, did you?"

Jack looked down, then reached out and ran a finger over the top of the desk in front of the typewriter. He could only shake his head. Then he quickly recoiled and yanked his hand away when he realized that he was destroying my furniture. A huge sliver was imbedded firmly in his finger.

"You have to be careful when you run your hand over an apple box," I cautioned him. "You're lucky you didn't end up with the whole board in your hand. Actually, I'd have used all orange crates if I could have gotten enough, but there was only one so I'm using it for my file cabinet. It's a two-drawer file cabinet. Obviously they build orange crates for just such an occasion." I smiled as I pointed to the partition that divided the box in half — each compartment was just big enough to hold files. "I'd offer you a chair, but the IGA

19

garbage pile didn't have any more crates. In a couple of days I should be able to get more boxes and make a counter. If I'm lucky, I may even be able to get another apple box for a chair. Here, c'mon, you look a little pale. Take a load off your feet and sit on my box."

"This is ridiculous!" Jack snorted in disgust. "When is your furniture supposed to be in?"

"No idea. I stopped in to see the Powers That Be yesterday, and they didn't know when, or even if it would be here this summer."

"Look," Jack said sympathetically, "come on over to the hotel and get a couple of tables and chairs. You can keep them as long as you need them."

"I don't know, Jack. That would mean that I'd be indebted to you. Some people might even suggest that I'm on the take. That I can be bought. I'm not sure that the Powers That Be would look too favourably on an officer putting himself in such a position. And, you know, when I look around the room, I'm kinda partial to this place now that I got it all fixed up. I think it has character. Don't you think it has character, Jack?"

"C'mon. Let's go," he said and headed out the door.

I followed Jack across the parking lot and reluctantly entered the Hinton Hotel barroom through the back door. Jack took the ashtrays off three beer tables, and we toted those tables back across the parking lot into the brand-new Fish and Wildlife Office. He kindly threw in half a dozen bar stools.

Now, beer tables are excellent places to set beer bottles and beer glasses. Even ashtrays and the odd pickled egg suit a beer table real well. However, beer tables are at best a dubious place for office supplies, as I was about to find out. One beer table served as my desk, the second became a work table for files, and the third was the counter. I stacked the apple boxes against the wall alongside the orange crate. Now I had both a filing cabinet and a set of bookshelves. All I needed were some files and some books.

With all my new office furnishings properly arranged, I perched on a bar stool behind a beer table, my desk. The old Underwood typewriter sat right in the middle of that beer table. No doubt about it, I thought, as I surveyed my kingdom, my brand-new office has all the earmarks of a great barroom. Minus the typewriter, there was nothing in it that remotely looked as if it belonged in a Fish and Wildlife office.

Pulling my bar stool up to the beer table, I reached forward for the typewriter keys. It was then I realized that as long as the typewriter remained in the middle of the round beer table, I couldn't reach the keys. Without a second's hesitation, I pulled the typewriter towards me. Big mistake. The weight of the typewriter on the edge of the table brought the whole works forward. Instantly, beer table and typewriter came crashing onto my lap. Somehow I managed to catch the typewriter. I sat there on the bar stool with the beer table lying in my lap and the typewriter in my arms, thanking the good Lord that the typewriter hadn't landed on the floor. If receiving office furniture in a timely fashion was any indication, chances are I might never have gotten another one.

"Great, just bloody great!" I cursed as I struggled to

21

get out from under the beer table and off the bar stool without dropping the typewriter.

I finally got the beer table returned to an upright position and the typewriter back onto the middle of it. I looked around the room to see what else I could manufacture into a typing desk. Except for the beer tables, the bar stools, the file cabinet, and the bookshelves, the room was still pretty bare.

I looked at the bookshelves. Well, I thought, I don't really have any books yet, and probably won't for some time, and those apple boxes are best suited to my typing needs. So the apple boxes won out over the beer tables.

"And to think," I said out loud, "Jack wanted me to throw those apples boxes back on the garbage pile. Let it be a lesson: Never throw out a good apple box." I chuckled to myself as I went about setting up the secretarial station. The beer tables and the bar stools would be for guests to sit and maybe have a drink. Coffee, of course—this is, after all, an official government office.

When the main office was properly set up, I took one last look around, then I turned out the lights, closing the office for the day. I opened the door to the storage room, my personal office, and closed the door behind me.

Alone in the privacy of the inner sanctum, I wasted little time. I plunked myself down in a corner next to my knapsack. Inside the knapsack I found what I was looking for—my old standby, a can of sardines. It didn't take me long to wolf down my not-so-gourmet meal of half a dozen little fish, and push the can to one side. I sighed as I leaned forward and took off my shoes and socks, and I wriggled my toes to give them a well-deserved airing. An aroma that could rival only the stink of the mill filled my office. I looked at my sweaty, wrinkly feet. Nah, I thought, it must be the sardines.

I stood up and stepped out of my trousers, folded them neatly and placed them in the corner on the floor that I had warmed up; unbuttoning my shirt, I draped it on top of the trousers. I dropped my shorts and stretched aching muscles — it's not easy sitting on an apple box all day. I did a couple of push-ups, just to prove I could still do them. Finally, I unrolled my sleeping bag, rolled up my baseball jacket for a pillow, set my old alarm clock, and turned out the light. For a second night I crawled into my bed, on the floor. I thought how absurd this looked.

I lay on my back on the hard linoleum floor and stared into the darkness. I could picture the majestic Canadian Rockies outside, to the west; and to the east, 500 miles away, I could see Mar and our two little girls in Saskatchewan. They were all sleeping, tucked away in warm, comfortable beds.

Suddenly the majestic Rocky Mountains paled by comparison to the sight and sounds of two little girls rushing to meet me at the end of the day. I missed my family. Man, I had to find a house, any house, and tomorrow would not be soon enough.

A 4x4, A LOT, AND MY FAMILY

"What the hell is this, lad?" roared one of the Powers That Be. He had burst through the door of the brand-new Fish and Wildlife Office in Hinton, but had stopped short, just inside the door. He was honouring me with his first visit, and to my surprise, dead silence followed his first words of greeting. Now he stood silent in the doorway, surveying the rather unique collection of office furnishings that I had gleaned and expertly arranged in the main office.

"Well, howdy, and a jolly good day to you too," I replied from where I sat perched on an apple box behind the desk, which consisted of two apple boxes, one stacked on top of the other. "Am I ever glad to see you. In fact, I just tried to phone you. I really need a 4x4 if I'm going to do anything meaningful in this country."

"Hmph," he grunted, and I watched as his eyes moved slowly around my office. They took in every item. He did not miss a single detail as he surveyed the room.

"I see! So, is this a social call, or are we talking business today?" I asked, since I had had no prior knowledge of his visit.

"How is everything?" he finally asked, ignoring my question.

"Oh, great, just great," I replied, lying through my teeth. "Other than needing a 4x4, some new office furniture, and a secretary, everything's just peachy-keen here. I am charging ahead around here just like I was in my right mind."

"Hmph," he grunted again, and his eyes began a second sweep of the office.

"Well, now that you've had a good look around, tell me, have you ever seen a finer Fish and Wildlife office in your whole life?" I asked. "You know, a person with an untrained eye may find it hard to believe, but I've actually got this place running like a well-oiled machine."

"Uh-huh," he replied, and walked over to one of the beer tables that served as my counter and interview table. He hesitated and shook his head, as if he could not believe what he was seeing. Then, as if he were weary, he plunked himself down on a bar stool.

"I'll bet you came to tell me that you're getting me a 4x4—or better yet, that you brought one with you," I said.

"I swear, lad, it looks like a bloody barroom in here. Where did you get this collection of junk from?" he asked. Once more he ignored my question as he deliberately ran his hand over the tabletop that bore battle scars from years of abuse. Then he examined his fingers as if he expected to find spilt beer.

"I'm glad you asked that question," I replied, as I

jumped at the opportunity he afforded me. "Let me start by — "

"No! No! Stop! On second thought, it's probably better if I didn't know," he quickly interjected before I had really got into my story. "I don't think I have the time or the stomach for it," he added in a surly tone. Obviously he didn't appreciate my humour. "I'm afraid to ask what you've done to the back office."

"Nothing," I replied quickly. "Jack over at the hotel couldn't spare any more beer tables or bar stools, and the IGA was out of apple boxes and orange crates. Anyway, since I don't have approval to hire a steno yet, I do all my entertaining right here in the front office. There's no need to use that office, so I've just locked it up for now."

I really didn't want him snooping around back there. Since arriving in Hinton, I had been unsuccessful in locating any kind of accommodation for myself, let alone my family. Being the thrifty sort, and making do with what was available, I had taken up temporary residence in the back office. The furnishings in the back were even more meagre than in the front: my shaving kit, a towel, my personal sleeping bag, and a really hard mattress, the tiled office floor.

"I need a coffee," he said, looking around. "Where do you keep the coffee pot?"

"Sorry, no coffee pot either. Maybe you could get the Department to toss one in, and you could bring it with my 4x4 — and give the secretary a ride, too. I'll bet that she'll even help you load the office furniture into the truck," I said, and smiled.

"Let's go, you can buy me a coffee," he snarled.

"Okay," I replied. "Anything for a man of adventure."

"What's that supposed to mean?" he snapped at me.

"It means getting a table in the restaurants in Hinton these days is an adventure that could take all day."

The lineup at the Hinton Hotel restaurant was shorter than usual, but it was still out the door.

"Let's go somewhere else," he said as we walked to the end of the line that stopped between two parked trucks, 4x4's. "A person could die of thirst waiting for a coffee here."

"You'll find the same thing in all the restaurants in this boom town," I said.

We stood in line, leaning against one of the trucks, and I took the opportunity to reinforce my need for a 4x4. I patted the box. Then I leaned over and checked the high suspension and large tires.

"Man, but I could sure use this beauty," I said. "You know, spring breakup was a total disaster for me. There's a lot of construction going on in this country and those big rigs are chewing up every road. Unless it's sunny and dry, I can't turn a wheel if I get off Highway 16. My Pontiac wasn't really built for running back roads through the foothills, the mountains, and the muskegs."

"Come on, lad, surely you can hitch a ride with somebody else if you need to go somewhere. I've always found people in these small towns to be very neighbourly," he said.

"Oh, sure, everybody's extremely friendly and more

27

than willing to lend a helping hand. The RCMP have a 4x4 Travelall, and whenever they have to go north they always ask if I'd like to go for a ride. And the Community Development officer — a provincial employee just like me — he was issued a Toyota 4x4, and I can go for a ride with him whenever he leaves town. The district health nurse and the guys from Forestry, they have 4x4s too. They're all great and I can catch a ride any time. Only I can't go where and when I need to go. I can only go where and when they need to go. For the most part, I can only go for a ride when it's convenient for someone else. Do you see my dilemma?"

Before he could reply, the manager of the restaurant approached us. I had been so busy talking and laying my tale of woe on my boss that I didn't realize that we had advanced and were at the head of the line.

"One?" he said to the Powers That Be, who was standing ahead of me.

"No, there's two of us," he replied.

"Take 'em as they come," the manager stated, "or move to the back of the line."

"That's the way it is around here these days," I said to him. "The guy at the head of the line gets the first available seat. Unless you're lucky enough to be here when two guys leave from the same table, you dine with strangers."

"Maybe I should wait," said the Powers That Be.

"Maybe you shouldn't if you want a cup of coffee today," I assured him.

And so, the Powers That Be followed the manager to the only available seat and sat down with three men that he had never seen before in his life. I smiled to myself as he sat down and introduced himself. The three never looked up, and the scene brought back memories of a couple of days earlier.

I had stopped at the restaurant for lunch and had waited for almost two hours until I was finally seated. At the table were three men that I had never seen before. One fellow had almost finished his meal, the other two had just received theirs. I, too, had introduced myself, but like the Powers That Be, I was ignored. My dining companions had more pressing matters on their minds.

"What'll you have?" asked the waitress, and without waiting for an answer she added, "If I was you, I'd take the special. It comes with soup and dessert."

"I think I'd like the special," I replied. I didn't have to ask what it was, as the other three were all eating Swiss steak, a heap of mashed spuds smothered with gravy, and creamed corn that covered the plate.

My meal had just arrived, complete with the bill, when the fellow sitting across from me finished his meal. He grabbed his bill, then stood up to leave, but he paused and looked back at the table.

"Any of you guys interested in buying a lot?" he asked.

"What kind of a lot?" I asked.

"A house lot. It's right behind the cop shop, on the hill," he said. "And it's got a two-car garage on it."

"How much you asking?"

"Twelve hundred dollars," he stated. "Sight unseen."

"I'll take it," I replied. It was the first lead I had had on any kind of accommodation since I had arrived in Hinton. As long as I could find a piece of land, I figured I could get someone to build me a house.

"Well, let's go and get your money," he said. "I'm leaving for Prince George and I want to get on the road."

"There's a lawyer down in the valley," I said. "I'll just finish my meal and meet you there."

"I'm going now — take it or leave it."

"I was just thinking the same thing," I replied. "We should really go see that lawyer right now." There was no doubt in my mind that the lot was far more important than the Swiss steak.

As I walked to the door, the two men remaining at our table started to argue over my untouched meal. I paid my bill and just as the fight started, I walked out the door. I got into my car and followed the guy to the law office in the valley.

Yes, I thought, had it not been for the seating arrangement of the day, I might never have gotten a lot or a place to live in Hinton — or for that matter, learned to build a house. I never did find a builder, but many a smashed finger and blackened fingernail attested to the fact that I did learn a thing or two about using a hammer and a saw the hard way.

"One?" barked the restaurant manager, jolting me back to reality.

"Right," I replied, and followed him to a seat at the opposite end of the restaurant from where the Powers That Be sat.

The Powers That Be and myself, we both had our coffees, sitting together at separate tables and drinking in silence. I watched as he got his bill, stood up, and walked over to where I was sitting.

"I'm leaving," he said as he dropped his bill in front of me. He was serious, I was buying.

"What about my 4x4?" I asked as he walked out of the restaurant.

"You'll get your 4x4 one of these days," he growled. "Just try to show a little patience."

Some many weeks later I received another visit. I looked up and was surprised to see the same Powers That Be come strutting into my office as if he owned the world. He had a huge, smug smile on his face, like the cat that ate the canary.

"Well, now, this is certainly better," he commented, looking around the office like a proud new father.

"It's an improvement from your last visit, isn't it?" I replied. The beer tables and bar stools had been returned to their rightful place in the Hinton Hotel barroom, and the apple boxes and the orange crates to the IGA garbage pile. Sometime, sandwiched between his two visits, I had finally received the furniture, although I did have to buy the coffee pot myself — and lo and behold, there was also a steno seated behind the new desk.

"As you can see," he said, and waved his arm before him covering the office, "I'm as good as my word. And oh, by the way, lad," he added as if it was no big deal, "I've got you that 4x4 you've been asking for."

He stood there grinning from ear to ear as he

31

casually raised his hand and dropped a set of keys on the counter.

"You're kidding me?" I shouted, not trying to conceal my enthusiasm. "A 4x4! A real honest-to-goodness 4x4, for me! Man, this is a gift beyond my wildest imagination. I've got to see it with my own two eyes to believe it. You know, I never for one minute thought that I'd ever get a 4x4. Where is it?" I asked, as I raced past him to the door and looked out. But there was no 4x4 in the parking lot or on the street. "I don't see it," I stated. "You're pulling my leg, aren't you?"

"Believe it, lad. It's true," he crowed. "It's a Dodge Power Wagon. I just drove it up and it's yours. Now, I don't want to hear you yappin' about never getting any equipment."

"Mum's the word, you can count on it," I yodelled happily.

"Good. That's the spirit, lad," he said.

"Well, where is it then?" I repeated, and walked outside for a better look. "I don't see no 4x4! In fact, there's nothing out here!"

"That's because I parked it over by the Pioneer store," he replied.

"The Pioneer store? Why'd you want to park it over there?" I asked, feeling disappointed that he would drive it to Hinton and not deliver such a prize right to my front door.

"I stopped to see my old friend Art Dunn at the Pioneer store and then I thought I'd walk over. It's such a nice day," he said, as if it was an everyday event. "Oh, by the way, Art said he would like to become a licence vendor. You better stop in and see him and have him make out an application for a vendorship when you pick up your truck. Art's a good guy to get to know; he can be very helpful. Art sells snow machines, you know, and he says you can borrow one of his any time you need to."

"What you're telling me is that I'm not going to get a Ski-Doo for this winter and you've made arrangements with one of your buddies, setting me up to go on the bum again, right?" I asked.

"Oh no," he quickly countered. "You'll get a Ski-Doo too. Just as soon as it comes in I'll bring it up. Just like I did with the 4x4. Your truck's the dark green Dodge Power Wagon, you can't miss it."

"Dark green! You don't mean 'Forestry green', do you?" I asked jokingly as I left the office to get my 4x4, and to talk to Art Dunn about the licence vendorship. Visions of a shiny new truck crowded my mind.

I was surprised to see Art standing out in front of the Pioneer store. It was as if he was waiting for me.

"So, what do you think of my new wheels?" I asked Art as we stood in front of his store looking at my Dodge Power Wagon, my Forestry green Dodge Power Wagon. "It may not look it, but I think she's a thing of beauty."

Art, however, could not see the beauty in the old truck, for it was anything but new. Actually, Art could hardly see anything through his tear-filled eyes. He was almost killing himself, he was laughing so hard.

"You're . . . you're taking this pretty well," he finally

choked out through fits of laughter. "If I were in your shoes, I'd be madder'n a hornet if somebody gave me a pile of junk like this to drive, especially alone in the bush," he howled, and then broke up again, leaning against the front of his store to keep from falling down.

Art was right, my new Dodge Power Wagon did look like it had a little wear and tear on it. In fact, it looked like it had been the second-last vehicle left in a demolition derby. The shiniest part on the entire vehicle was on both doors where the decals had been removed. Decals that, I had no doubt, had previously identified my not-so-new 4x4 as one belonging to the Alberta Forest Service.

"Why don't you get in and fire it up," Art roared from his leaning position against the front of the store. "I'd like to go along when you take her for a spin."

"Sure, why don't I do that," I replied. "Get in and I'll fire her up."

"That's okay," he howled. "I'll just wait here."

"Now, why do I have this feeling that you know something I don't?" I asked suspiciously. I was getting a real sinking feeling in the pit of my stomach.

"Beats me—" Art started, but he couldn't continue as spasms of laughter gripped his body. He had to wait until he could calm himself before he added, "I think you should really get in and turn it over—the best is yet to come."

The door squeaked and squealed when I pulled on the door handle. Suddenly there was a loud crack as it grudgingly swung open. "That's nothing a little oil won't fix," I mentioned to Art.

Art just howled.

Very carefully, I climbed into the cab of the old crate, inserted the key into the ignition, and reached for the starter. "Please Lord, let it start," I prayed. "At least let it start and run long enough so I can get away from here."

RRRRR, cough, sputter, sputter, cough, RRRRR. The motor groaned weakly each time I pushed the starter. "No such luck," I moaned and closed my eyes, trying to hide the image of Art, who was now clinging to the side of the building, he was laughing so hard. Art, at least, was enjoying this moment. To him, this was a moment to savour.

"You . . . you know, when your boss got ready to leave here earlier this morning, he said he was going to take the truck over to your office. Said he couldn't wait to see the look in your eyes when he delivered your 4x4, but then he couldn't get it started either," Art howled, and the tears rolled down his cheeks. "We worked on it for about half an hour. I don't know what's wrong with it."

"You're kidding me, aren't you?" I asked.

"No, I'm not. I'm dead serious." He roared again.

"I think the battery is just about dead now," Art offered. "He was grinding 'er pretty good trying to get 'er started. Maybe you can get Forestry to give you some tips on how to get 'er going." He laughed some more.

Art was turning into quite a comedian, I thought as I got out of the truck and the door once more squeaked and squealed when I tried to close it. I had to slam the bloody thing about a dozen times before the latch finally caught. I left my 4x4 and Art in front of the Pioneer store and returned to my office the way I had come, on foot.

A request to appear before the Powers That Be was never taken lightly. The reason for the invite was not always clear, and long ago I had learned that it was wise to be alert. And alert I was, bright-eyed and bushy-tailed, when I entered the office after I had received my 4x4, to answer the summons.

"Hi, you want to see me?" I asked as I walked into the office.

"Good morning, lad," greeted the Powers That Be, extending his hand. "Have a seat, lad. How's everything going?"

"Not bad," I replied. "No sense complaining, nobody listens anyway."

"I was just wondering . . ." he began, and then hesitated. "Have . . . have you talked to Art Dunn lately?"

"No . . . no, as a matter of fact I haven't seen him since, oh, let me see now . . . oh yes, it was last week. As I recall, he was leaning on the front of a Forestry green Dodge 4x4. Why, is there something wrong?" I asked in my most surprised voice.

"I've talked to Art a couple of times . . ." he paused and gave me a really stern look. "Art . . . well, Art says he thinks that maybe you're trying to avoid him. Are you?"

"Me?" I asked. Now I was really surprised. "Avoiding Art? Why would I want to do a thing like that. After all, if I want to get around this winter, I'm gonna have to borrow one of his snow machines. No, I'm not avoiding him. Did he say there was any particular reason for feeling that way?"

"No, he didn't, but I was wondering, have you talked to him about the licence vendorship?"

"That's it," I said, snapping my fingers. "The licence vendorship. Dang it anyway. You know, I was so excited about that 4x4 you got me, I forgot all about him wanting a vendorship. You know, he never even mentioned it, and . . . darn anyway, I blew it. I forgot it completely. I'll bet he's sore about it, what did he say?"

"Nothing, he didn't even mention the vendorship," he replied. "That's why I asked you to come in. You know, Art's a pretty good guy to know, he can be a lot of help to you."

"Yeah, I know. That's my fault," I replied apologetically. "I'll get on it as soon as I get back to Hinton. Leave it with me — it's as good as done."

"Good. Good. You got to keep the locals happy, you know," he smiled. "Now, how do you like your new truck? How's it running?"

"Truck?" I asked. "I don't have a truck. I've only got a car."

"No, not your vehicle, the truck. You know, the 4x4 I got you," he said.

"Oh yes, that truck! You mean the Forestry green Dodge Power Wagon? The one you left parked in front of the Pioneer store last week?"

"Yeah, that's the one, the one I brought you last week," he replied. "How's it working?"

"I don't know," I replied as deadpan as I could.

"What do you mean, you don't know?"

"I mean, I don't know," I replied. "But that's something I was going to talk to you about. I'm glad you reminded me." Then I stood up and slowly took the keys from my pocket. I dangled them over his desk, then dropped them.

"Here now, lad, what's this?" he asked, taken aback.

"These, sir, are the keys to a Forestry green Dodge 4x4 that you parked on the street in front of the Pioneer store in Hinton," I replied.

"I don't want them," he declared and shoved them back across the desk towards me.

"Me neither," I said, smiling at him. "So I'm returning the keys in the same condition I got them."

"What's the matter, I thought you wanted a 4x4?" he growled. I could sense a change in his mood.

"I did and I still do. But I want a 4x4 that runs. One that will get me home, if I could ever get it started."

"What do you mean? That truck still has lots of good miles left in it if a man knows how to take care of it," he declared.

"That appears to be a matter of opinion," I replied. "You see, I checked with Forestry, the previous owner. They feel a little different. They tell me that truck's been parked for the past six months because it was costing them a fortune to keep it running. That, of course, was when they could get it running. They think it's funnier than all get-out that I've got it now. In fact, I'm beginning to think that I must be one great comedian, because every time I meet a forest officer on the street or walk into a room where one happens to be, he bursts out laughing. 'How's that brand new 4x4 of yours running?' or 'Are you still using the street in front of the Pioneer for a parking lot?' one will ask, and then everybody within earshot laughs like it's the funniest thing they ever heard."

"You know, that truck was a steal," he stated. "I got it for a dollar."

"You got taken," I assured him. "They would have paid you five just to get rid of it."

"I don't think that's the least bit funny," he snapped.

"Me neither."

"I take it you don't want it, then?" he asked, sounding disappointed.

"You got that right," I assured him.

"You have to remember that it's not an easy task to get your hands on a good used 4x4 these days. But if you don't want it, then someone else can have it."

"Don't forget to give that someone else my sincere condolences, because they're going to need it," I answered.

"Well . . . if that's the way you feel, I'm not one to force good equipment on anybody, especially someone that doesn't appreciate it. You'll be the loser on this one, lad," he said, and he picked up the keys. "Where'd you park it?"

"I didn't," and I smiled, "you did. And I'll bet Art would help you push it all the way across the street just to get rid of it from in front of his store."

THE SPECIAL MOOSE LICENCE

At eleven o'clock on a Friday night, most normal people working a government job in a small town would be celebrating the end of their workweek. It worked for me, and after all, I figured I was normal. The office was closed for the weekend, and so it appeared was the District, even though I had just finished the first few days of the hunting season.

"I can certainly see why mountain districts are the sacred cows," I said to Mar as I stretched back on the sofa. "If this is what they're all like, I'll gladly spend the rest of my days in the mountains."

The opening few days of the hunting season had been nothing like what I had experienced in Brooks and Strathmore, where vehicles lined the roads and trails, and hunters swarmed the countryside. Although I had found hunters, they were few and far between in the forests of the foothills and the mountains. In fact, if Strathmore had been the old folks' home, Hinton had to be the morgue. In my previous six years I had never been home with my family on a Friday night during the hunting season.

"Hall of fame! Who in the hall do you want?" was my flippant greeting when the phone rang just as the eleven o'clock news was coming on television. I was in a mellow mood, settling into a life of leisure in the good district. That everything was good was evident in the fact that it was I and not Mar who answered the phone — Mar had been screening my calls in Strathmore for the past four years.

"A-are you the game warden?" asked a hesitant voice on the other end of the line. Obviously the caller had not spoken to many happy game wardens at that hour of the night.

"That I am," I replied. "And who might you be?"

"Boy, am I glad we found you," said the voice, sounding relieved. "We need some of those special moose licences."

"Special moose licences?" I repeated and immediately racked my brain, trying to identify that particular licence. It for sure was not a licence I was familiar with; but then, there never had been many moose in the Strathmore district. "Special moose licence," I muttered to myself.

"You know, that special moose licence. I understand it costs twenty-five dollars," he said.

"Oh yeah, right, you mean that Special Moose

41

Licence," I said, remembering that I had checked it off when the licences came in. I had given it a passing glance. It was a new licence in the ever-increasing number of different, never-before-seen-or-heard-of licences that seemed to arrive every year. There rarely seemed to be any information to explain their existence. In my experience, there had never been a great demand for a new licence, at least not in the first year, so I had just dismissed them. However, I should have paid attention, for this licence was indeed special — it was an opportunity for a non-resident to hunt a moose, any age, any sex, for a nominal fee.

"Yes, sir," I said. "The new twenty-five-dollar Special Moose Licence. That will be no problem at all. I do have lots of them, and you can pick one up when the office opens on Monday morning at eight o'clock sharp."

"Oh, man, we can't wait that long," moaned the voice. "Isn't there somewhere else we can get a licence?"

"I'm afraid not," I replied. "I'm it, and the office won't be open until Monday."

"Please, you gotta help us. We've been driving since Thursday night, we took today off work, and we've got to be back to work on Monday morning. You've got to help us, man," he said pleading.

"Where are you from?" I asked.

"We're up from Seattle in Washington state, and we'd sure be obliged if you could sell us some of those special licences," he replied.

"Even if I get you the licences tonight, you would still have to have a guide," I informed him. "I don't suppose you've got a guide, do you?"

"We sure have. We called up this fella and he says he's a Class 'A' guide. Whatever that is. Anyway, he said to just call you up when we got into town. As soon as we can get our licences, we're off to meet him."

"All rightee, then," I said, and chuckled. "You know where my office is?"

"You bet we do." He sounded happy and relieved. "We're calling from the hotel next door."

"I'll be down to the office in a few minutes," I told him.

"You're not going down to the office at this hour, are you?" Mar asked before I even hung up the receiver.

"I shouldn't be long," I said to Mar, giving her a little peck on the cheek. "There's a couple of Yanks down at the office looking for licences. I guess issuing a couple of licences beats sitting on a roadblock till the wee hours of the morning. I'll be back shortly."

But I was wrong on both counts. I had forgotten it was a Friday night. The streets and the parking lot in front of the hotel and behind it, as well as around my office, were crammed with vehicles — trucks and campers of every type imaginable. There was no place for the Fish Cop in front of his own office. I had to park on the next street, in front of the IGA Foodliner, and walk back. And there were men standing in front of my door on the steps. They were everywhere.

"What is this?" I asked the first person I encountered as I walked past and around vehicles, all of which seemed to have Washington licence plates. "You fellas having a convention here, or is this a mass migration from the States? I'll bet there's nobody left in Washington. I hope the last guy turned out the light when he left."

"Oh, there's a bunch more where we come from," he replied happily.

"Are you guys all together?" I asked him. I couldn't believe how many vehicles and people there were. There had to be at least thirty trucks and fifty, maybe sixty men. Before I got the door unlocked, another rig pulled up.

"He belong to your bunch too?" I joked.

"Oh no, I don't know but a couple of these guys. I've never seen the rest of these men before in my life," he said, and chuckled.

I had to push my way through the crowd, as those nearest the door seemed to be reluctant to lose the spot they occupied. Finally, I was able to open the office door and the horde crowded in behind me.

"I can't believe this," I said, shaking my head. "What would make all of you want to come here to hunt moose, and on the same night too. You guys know something I don't?"

"We're here to help you kill some of them there moose, since you got so many," one of them responded enthusiastically.

"How'd you figure that?" I said, thinking of the number of people I knew who hadn't filled their tags last year.

"It says so, right here in your ad," one of them

replied, and showed me a newspaper clipping that quoted one of the Powers That Be.

Come to Alberta and help us harvest an overpopulation of moose! read the ad. Then it went on to say, *There's virtually a moose behind every tree in northern Alberta.*

I had to read it again. I couldn't believe what I had read the first time. I looked at all the faces of the eager hunters who were packed into the waiting area. Another group arrived and tried to push their way in.

I whistled. "This is unbelievable! How many of you gentlemen have to be at work on Monday morning?" A chorus of "Me"s indicated that they all had to. "Well, let's try this — is there anybody here that doesn't have to be at work Monday morning?" There was no response. I just shook my head. "Hopefully I can get you all licences before Monday."

"We hope so, too. We been driving a long time," someone said. "We left home early this morning and drove up through Banff and Jasper. It sure is pretty coming through those mountains."

"How do we get a licence to shoot one of those elk we seen all over the highway back a piece?" someone asked.

"Those are in Jasper National Park," I informed them. "If you get caught hunting in there you won't have to worry about going to work on Monday morning. Those park wardens are some pretty mean dudes. They'll lock you up and throw away the key. They don't have a very good sense of humour when it comes to shooting their animals."

"I think we're gonna be here for awhile," I said, "If any of you need some groceries or gas, you may want to try finding something open while I start with the licences."

"We got everything," replied a voice. "We brought everything we need with us."

"Well, I'm sure you're gonna need a little gas, my friend," I chuckled. "It's a long way between gas stations once you head north, and you can't start hunting till you get north of the Berland River into Zone 1."

"We brought gas, too," he replied. "All we need now is a licence."

"You brought gas, too?" I asked in disbelief. "How?"

"We brought a couple of drums with us. You don't have to worry about us, we got plenty of everything."

"I don't believe any of this. You fellows sure this is for real? I must be dreaming!" I exclaimed.

"We're for real all right, and as soon as we get our licences we'll be out of your hair," somebody in the back quipped.

"Okay, fellas, two things you should know before we start. Exchange rates and guides," I began, speaking loud enough for everyone to hear my little spiel. "Now, this is important, so listen up. First and foremost, I have absolutely no idea what the exchange rate is and I can't get it tonight. Even if I could, it would change by Monday. The last time I got involved with the exchange rate on a weekend, I used a Friday quote. By Monday, when I took the money to the bank, the rate had changed and I ended up paying the difference myself.

Now, I don't mind helping you boys out by coming down and selling you licences, but I won't help you pay for them. The licence is twenty-five dollars, US or Canadian. If you don't have Canadian funds, then I would suggest you all go over to the hotel—it's right next door—and the manager there will be only too happy to exchange your money. I will be happy to accommodate anybody who insists on exchange from me on Monday, as soon as the bank opens and I can establish a rate. Any questions?" Nobody said a word, nobody left to go next door to the hotel.

"Now, the second point: You boys all know that you have to have a guide with you when you're hunting. Just for the record, and for your own protection and safe return, I want you to understand that anybody caught hunting without a guide won't make it back for work on Monday morning." They all thought this was quite funny and it got a good laugh.

The first twenty-five US dollars hit the table.

"If you don't quit jabbering and start selling them licences, I'm still going to be standing in this door on Monday morning," said a disgruntled voice from the back of the room.

"One last thing—I trust you all know that if you should be lucky enough to get a moose on your one-day hunt, you'll have to have an export permit before you leave Alberta."

"Where do we get that?" someone asked.

"You get that right back here, gentlemen, and this office doesn't open till Monday morning. So you better pray that you can find me and I'm in a good mood. But

47

during the hunting season, and particularly the way this one is starting, I wouldn't be counting too heavily on it."

It was well past four in the morning when the last hunter dropped his twenty-five dollars on the counter. I dragged my butt out of the office, thanking the good Lord that it was still dark. It was time for sleep.

The odd Saturday morning that I didn't work belonged to me and my daughters. It was Mar's morning to sleep in, and I got to spend some quality time with Kelly and Robin. Having worked half the night, I had absolutely no intention of working this Saturday morning.

I was tired and did not just bounce out of bed with my usual enthusiasm, but my daughters did. With tons of encouragement from those two little girls, I crawled slowly out of my nice, warm, comfortable bed, and we got dressed. I thought it would be nice to sit in the living room among the building materials, and just relax with a coffee. The girls were each drinking a glass of milk when I wandered into the construction zone, or as we lovingly called it, our living room. There, from force of habit, I foolishly pulled aside the white sheet hanging over the window.

Instantly, I stopped and stared in horror at the scene that greeted me. There were trucks and campers parked in front of my house, in front of the church, in front of the neighbours' houses, down the street and around the corner. Realizing my error, I quickly dropped the sheet again. Too late—I had been spotted. Two men who had been standing point in front of my house jumped too,

48

and made straight for the door. This is a nightmare, I thought, and I opened the front door before their pounding woke Mar.

"Is the game warden here?" one of them asked.

"I'm not sure," I replied. "Who wants to know?"

"Hey, that's pretty good," he laughed. "We thought we'd catch you before you left for the day. We need some of them special moose licences."

"Don't tell me. Let me guess," I said. "You need them right away because you're from Washington state and you have to be back to work on Monday morning."

"Yeah. That's right. How'd y'all know that?"

"Just a lucky guess," I grumbled. "How many guys need licences?"

"I don't know, but there's a bunch!" He chuckled. "You might want to pack lunch when you come to the office."

"That I can see. Well, I haven't had breakfast yet, so you go on down to the office and wait. I'll be along as soon as I'm finished."

"That could be the last time I open the drapes during this hunting season," I muttered to myself as I turned from the door.

It seemed to me that I had just left the office, and here I was back in it again, with the waiting area crammed full of Yanks.

Judging by the number of non-resident hunters who had come through my office in the past twelve hours, I didn't think it was possible for all of them to get a guide. For certain, many of them would not make it to Zone 1 before they started hunting.

49

I should have packed a lunch, because it was after noon before I left the office and returned home. There, however, I did pack a lunch and headed out to check hunters south of the Berland River. This area was closed to those hunting under the authority of the special licence and I figured it had to be crawling with Special Moose Licence hunters.

Hinton was a one-officer district, without a 4x4 and without any type of radio communication. Whenever I questioned the Powers That Be regarding these shortcomings, I always got the same reply: "Don't worry, lad. We're working on it."

One didn't go far into the bush with a car, and on this Saturday I patrolled north of Hinton, going as far as the Berland River. The weather was good, allowing me to stray off the beaten path. I encountered a few resident hunters before turning back to the Lower Hay River Road and on to the airstrip. There were plenty of fresh tracks showing that a number of vehicles had forded the Wildhay River just downstream from the confluence with Pinto Creek.

As usual, I stood on the south bank of the Wildhay River and stared longingly across. I would have loved to check out the north bank, but this was one of the fords that I could not make without a 4x4. As I had always done at this point, I turned back.

I had found one person fishing without a licence in Pinto Creek, the sum of my efforts for the day. I had checked all of the side roads, the cut lines, and the seismic trails. There was not a sign of a Washington licence plate or a Yankee hunter outside of Zone 1. The horde had simply vanished into the northern forest.

On my return to Hinton shortly after midnight, from force of habit I drove to the office to drop off the exhibits. As I turned the corner, I knew I should have driven home, locked the doors, and turned out the lights. The sight before me was incredible, a rerun from the night before, and I stopped in the middle of the street and stared. I could not believe my eyes. Once more there were trucks and men and there was no room for me.

"This is insane," I mumbled. "Where are these guys coming from?" My first thoughts were to keep on driving right on past and out of town again. But once more I parked in front of the IGA and walked back to my office.

Several of the trucks I walked past had legs, moose legs, sticking out of them. Obvious signs of a successful hunt, I deduced. I could only shake my head when I realized how many of them had been successful and would indeed be back in time for work on Monday morning. It was absolutely incredible.

As I walked across the street, through the parking lot, and up the steps to unlock the door, they piled out of their vehicles and fell in behind me. I turned on the lights and unlocked the cash drawer. "What'll it be, gentlemen?" I asked the first group.

"We need some of them special moose licences."

"How many need licences?" I raised my voice so that everyone could hear. About half the group shouted and raised their hands.

"Everyone here who needs a licence and has to be back to work Monday morning raise your hand." Not one hand went up. "The first thing we're going to do is issue export permits. We'll get the guys who have to be back to work Monday morning out of here, then we'll get to licences. Is everybody good with that?"

"I'm not," said one of the men who had forced his way to the counter.

"That's too bad," I replied and gave him my best sympathetic look. "Well, since we don't allow hunting on Sundays in Alberta, even if I were to give you a licence now, you couldn't use it until Monday. And you're in luck—the office opens at eight o'clock Monday morning, so you can pick your licence up then. Anybody else got a problem with me issuing the export permits first?" For some strange reason, everyone else was agreeable.

"Thank you, gentlemen," I said. "Now, if we could have those needing export permits to the front, maybe we can all get a little sleep yet tonight. Let's move it, gentlemen, I'm hungry and want to get home." There was a shuffling of bodies as those wanting export permits moved to the front of the counter and those wanting licences moved to the back.

It was breakfast time when I finally left the office. I was starving, having missed both supper and a midnight snack. But it was not to be. Before I even got to my street I saw the lineup. Where have these guys been all night while I was at the office? I asked myself. I was not very happy as I drove past and waved for them to follow me. This was one long, miserable ordeal as I opened the office for the fourth time in the past thirty hours.

I didn't get any supper or breakfast; I was just too tired, and I crashed when I got home. I woke around noon and walked out into the kitchen. "Do you want to have some breakfast before you go to the office, or when you come back?" Mar asked me.

"I'm not going to the office," I muttered, and looked at her like she'd lost it. "What would I want to go down there for? I've spent enough time there in the past two days to last me for a lifetime."

"Well, you're going to spend some more. I've told several people who have phoned that you'd be down as soon as you got up, and there have been several at the door."

"Oh no," I moaned. "Please tell me you're kidding. How many?"

"I have no idea, but I'd say you'll be lucky to get home by suppertime."

"I think I'll eat first," I grumbled, "but please, cook slow."

"We was told that you'd fix us up with a guide," said the first person I talked to when I arrived at the office.

"Who told you that nonsense?" I asked.

"I don't know," he replied. "All the guides we phoned were already busy, so we phoned the number that was in the ad. The lady that answered it said to contact you when we got here. She said you knew all the guides. You just tell us who to call and we'll call one right now." It was the first time anyone had indicated that he didn't have a guide.

"Sorry, fellows, I can't help you, all the guides I know are already booked up. I can sell you a licence, but the guide is up to you. If you don't have a guide, you may want to think twice because I don't have a truck or a 4x4, and I'll have yours if you try hunting on your own." Right, I thought, an idle threat. At the rate I was going, I'd never get out of the office.

That night, when I finally returned home for supper, I stuck a sign with big bold letters on the office door:

OFFICER OUT OF TOWN
OFFICE WILL BE OPEN
MONDAY MORNING 8:00 A.M.
SPECIAL MOOSE LICENCES
AVAILABLE 45 MILES EAST AT EDSON

"If anyone phones or comes to the door," I told Mar as I walked over and drew the drapes, "I'm out of town."

The first half-dozen or so calls were from hunters; then the locals and service station operators, started to call.

"I don't care who it is, Yank or local, I'm not home for anyone. I'm not going back to the office anymore this weekend."

"Well, I'm not going to lie anymore," Mar stated firmly. And shortly after eight she took the phone off the hook and turned out the lights. The first vehicle pulled up in front of the house a short time later. We sat in the dark, prisoners in our own house. Trucks and campers continued to drive by, searching for a parking spot. Next morning, I had an escort — they followed me to the office like a funeral procession.

I had to push my way through the mass of humanity that was already in the office. I felt sorry for the poor steno — she was not prepared for the Monday morning onslaught that swarmed through the doors. That morning she paid a dear price for getting to the office early. Her normal quiet, peaceful Monday morning routine of weekly reports, time sheets, and revenue returns was totally destroyed. It was only eight o'clock and already she looked frazzled. Hunters were demanding Special Moose Licences and export permits. And the lone phone was ringing off the wall. I disappeared into my office to answer it.

"What's come over you, lad? What do you think you're doing, putting a sign on your door and leaving your district without telling me?" It was an unexpected call from the Powers That Be.

"What have you done to me?" I asked, ignoring his questions. "This mountain district is crazy! I've been invaded by Yanks! They're nuts about this Special Moose Licence! My family needs some peace and quiet! I need help! I need more Special Moose Licences! I don't have enough left to last me the day. Send everything you've got."

"Slow down," he cautioned me. "Let's take one thing at a time, lad. You say you need more Special Moose Licences?"

"Send me all you've got — today. I doubt that I have enough to handle the people who are in the office right now, let alone the hordes that I'm sure are following," I replied.

"If what you're saying is true, it sounds like the new program is a success." I could just see his chest puffing out like that of a new father.

"Success? It's chaos!" I snorted. "My family hasn't had a minute's rest since Friday."

"Don't worry, lad. We'll get you more licences. We'll have them out there in a couple of days," he said.

"No! No, you don't understand, this is an emergency. We've been overrun with hunters from Washington. They're in here like a plague of locusts. My office is full of them. They're swarming the town. I think they're multiplying like rabbits. I need them licences now, today," I pleaded. "Get them out on the bus today, or get someone to drive them out. I don't care how you do it, just get them out here today, please."

"We'll do our best," he said. "We'll try to get them on the bus today."

"What about some help, will that be on the bus too?" I asked.

"You hang in there, lad. This is the first weekend. It will probably all blow over by tonight. You just calm down, tomorrow will be another day. You're not the only one that has had to work this morning. Thanks to you the Edson office is busy, too. They had about a dozen hunters in here already this morning. Can you believe that some of them even phoned last night? They said that you put the phone numbers of staff on that sign on your door. You didn't do that, did you?"

THE SPECIAL MOOSE LICENCE

"Well, I'm glad to hear some of them could read," I said. There was dead silence before he answered.

"You didn't have a sign posted on your door with names and numbers, did you, lad?"

"You know, in a moment of weakness I might have done something like that."

"Y-you can't do that," he sputtered. "You're there to provide a public service. Y-you can't give out private numbers just like that!"

"Oh darn, and here I was hoping that you were going to say that you were sending someone out to help me." My request was greeted by silence, so I continued. "Oh, and by the way, this successful Special Moose Licence is creating another problem that has to be addressed. Right now there's not a guide to be had in this country, and the hunters are complaining."

"We'll see what we can do about the guides, lad. You hang in there, now."

"And the last thing—when am I getting a 4x4?" I asked. I never passed up the chance to ask that question, even though the answer was always the same.

"We're working on it, lad. We're working on it," he said, and there was a click. The line went dead. He was gone.

The influx continued. When I wasn't at the office, the phone at the house never stopped ringing. Mar was constantly meeting another strange face at the door, and there were endless lines of trucks on the street in front of our house. The complaints about the lack of licensed guides increased. The hunters expected and wanted what they had been promised: a moose behind every tree, a guide, and a place to purchase a licence and get some information.

I was beginning to have a recurring dream. In it I could see myself gladly choking the guy who told me that the best districts were those with mountains. The Hinton district was a madhouse — and I must have been insane to have asked for it.

Finally, the Division responded: If there are no licensed guides available, non-resident alien special licence moose hunters will be allowed to swear an affidavit stating that they have tried and were unsuccessful in their attempts to obtain guiding service. They will then be authorized to hunt without the services of a guide. It was a handwritten note from the steno, the latest directive from the Powers That Be.

"That should take care of one problem from this maniacal hunt!" I said. Then I carefully folded the note and filed it in File 13, the garbage pail.

The following Saturday evening I returned from a trip north of Hinton. It was already past ten, but I knew there was no sense going home; the onslaught of the first week had not abated. I knew what was waiting for me. I went directly to the office. I turned the corner and was surprised to see that the office lights were on, and to my horror the office was packed, jammed full of hunters. "Oh no!" I cursed out loud and my first thought was "I forgot to lock the bloody door?"

I pushed my way through the crowd, and there behind the counter strewn with export permits and Special Moose Licences stood the steno.

"What's going on?" I asked. "Why are you here?"

"They came to my house and said they needed export permits and they couldn't wait for you to return."

"So you decided to play the Good Samaritan, did you? You know you shouldn't have done this. I don't have any money to pay you overtime."

"But they wouldn't leave. They told me if I would do this for them they'd each give me a couple of dollars. I would have done it just to get them away from my house!"

"Okay, if that's what they said. You go for it, girl — it's your show!"

I stood back and watched as each successful hunter came up, dropped a couple of bucks on the table, got an export permit, and thanked her most graciously for coming out. The line of hunters wanting export permits was almost done when one particular individual walked up to the counter.

"I think you've already got enough for what you've done tonight," he said to the steno as he laid his licence on the table. "I'll just take the export permit, thank you."

"Okay," she replied and started to fill out the export permit.

"Just a moment," I said, intervening in the transaction. "Correct me if I'm wrong, but my understanding is that this little lady left her house and family at your request and, I might add, most generous offer. At this hour of the night, this isn't her job and the government isn't paying her for her time. She doesn't have to be here, and frankly, neither do I." I picked up his licence and handed it back to him. "This office opens Monday morning at eight o'clock, sir. You can pick up an export permit then, unless you can find someone else to issue you one. Now, you have a good evening. Next!" I called out.

He stood there and looked at me and didn't move. "Next!" I called again. There was a considerable amount of shuffling and movement from the back of the pack, then no one moved. All eyes were on me, and it was so quiet you could hear a pin drop.

"Gentlemen, unless someone else steps forward, I'm going to clear this office out and no one gets a permit or licence tonight."

I looked back at the individual who was still standing at the counter. His mouth hung open as if he couldn't believe what was happening.

"Now, mister, you're standing in the way. Would you please move." He stepped aside. There was no hesitation as the next successful hunter jumped up to the counter.

I sat back on the corner of the desk again and looked around the room. Now everybody was standing there with a couple of bucks in hand. It looked as if everyone was going to make sure that I could see they had their two bucks ready. They were taking no chances. When a hunter wanting a licence laid two bucks on the table, I stepped forward.

"One moment, please," I said, much to his surprise and horror.

"I'll pay the two dollars," he blurted out. "I don't

mind compensating this nice lady for giving up her time."

"In good time, my friend," I said, "in good time. But first, is there anybody else who needs an export permit?" I looked around the room. Hunters were glancing at each other. "No one else for an export permit?" I repeated the question.

"Just me," came a voice from the side of the room. It was the successful hunter I had told to come back on Monday morning and he started to step forward.

"I told you, you can come back at eight o'clock on Monday morning. Eight o'clock, that's when the office opens."

"Okay," I said to the steno. "If that's all the export permits, you can go home now. No sense you standing here all night. I'll take care of the licences. Licences are twenty-five dollars, gentlemen. There's no need for the extra couple of bucks, I won't accept them."

"It's okay. I don't mind staying," offered the steno as she grabbed a pad of Wildlife Certificates and a sheet of Special Moose Licences.

"Suit yourself, but it's not necessary. And as I said, gentlemen, you pay for the licences only."

The first hunter had already put a couple of bucks on the counter and when he got his licence he pushed it towards the steno. "No thanks," she replied and smiled at him. "I can't accept that."

"I insist," he answered. "It's for you. I really appreciate you coming out here tonight. I want you to have it." He raced from the counter.

There was no stopping them. Each in their turn came

up and got a licence and left a couple of bucks on the counter. I stepped back from the counter and watched.

When the last Special Moose Licence was issued, there was still one person standing in the office with a couple of bucks in his hand.

"I'll give her a couple of bucks," snarled a very unhappy man.

"I'm sorry, sir," I replied. "I wouldn't want you to compromise yourself. The office will be open Monday morning at eight. You can get one then." He stared at me for a minute and then left.

"What am I going to do with this?" asked the steno as she looked at the stack of one-dollar bills that had accumulated on the counter.

"That's up to you," I smiled at her. "It's all yours. You better take them with you."

"Are you sure?"

"Absolutely. You can rest assured not one of those guys would have left me even one teensy little smell. From now on you can handle all these late calls. They treat you much better than they treat me," I grumbled.

"You're getting pretty grouchy," she informed me. "I think maybe you need a day off."

"Right," I replied. "Let's see, this is the second week of the Special Moose hunting season. There's still two months left. If I'm lucky, I'll get a day off in January."

"SHE'S A CLASS 'A' GUIDE"

The twenty-five-dollar Special Moose Licence had changed the hunting dynamics considerably in the Hinton Fish and Wildlife district. With the introduction of that one licence, Hinton lost its innocence and the appeal that made mountain districts so attractive. The guiding industry—tightly regulated, controlled, and predictable, so sacred to many—was blindsided. Within days, this tight community was flipped upside down, turned inside out, tossed over on its ear, and thrown out with the bathwater. Guiding and outfitting in Alberta would never be the same.

Monday mornings in this choice mountain district were uncharacteristically chaotic, to say the least. A person could bet his last dollar that the parking lots and the streets around the Fish and Wildlife Office and the Hinton Hotel would be jammed full of vehicles bearing

Washington state licence plates. All available space not occupied by a vehicle would be crowded with men.

In the few short days since the hunting season began, I had come to expect the unexpected every day. And I had not yet been disappointed. I knew from the moment I unlocked the door that today was going to be another long day at the counter. The horde of hunters pushed into the office behind me. All Yanks, all looking for Special Moose Licences. They crowded the counter.

And then there were the guides, the newly created Class 'B' guides. They were mostly young men from the Metis settlement at Marlboro, about thirty miles to the east. Every Monday morning the local Community Development officer would bring a number of them to Hinton. They had no vehicles, no equipment of any type, and many of them had never been in the bush north of Hinton, but nonetheless they were the guides. They were there to meet the demands of the massive number of hunters that were looking for the Special Moose Licences. The guides, new to the industry, were mostly shy young fellows. They followed the hunters through the door, then stood to one side quietly, patiently, waiting for a call that would signal a job for the next few days.

I unlocked the counter door, took out a pad of Wildlife Certificates and a sheet of Special Moose Licences, and opened the cash box. It was crammed with American money from the weekend sales. Then I looked up and wondered what twist this day would bring. I didn't have long to wait for the first gem of the day.

"You people aren't very accommodating," said one of the men in the first group of hunters. "You treat your guests poorly. I would have thought that licences would be more available. We've been waiting hours for you to open this place."

"I'll make a note of that, sir," I replied, "and I'll let the Powers That Be know that you're unhappy. I'm sure that they'll do something to correct that oversight. Now the best I can do is get you licensed up and on your way. Do you have a driver's licence?"

"Hold on, now," he quickly interjected. "We just need some information on them Special Moose Licences. Once we've had a chance to study it, then we'll think about getting some licences."

"Suit yourself," I replied. "But if you're in a hurry, maybe I can help. By now I'm sure I've heard every question. I might even have some of the answers."

"If you could just give us the information, we'll read up on it ourselves. We're in no hurry."

"No problem," I replied, and handed him and his two companions each a package of the information they required. I proceeded to sell licences to the rest. The odd group had already contacted a guide before they arrived; they picked up their licences and left. The rest would pick up a licence, then turn to the Class 'B' guides who stood waiting to one side. They would contract the guide to ride around in their vehicle until their hunt was over. Once they left, I would not see the guide again until the following Monday.

By noon, there were still a few Class 'B' guides left. The horde of hunters, with the exception of the first threesome, were gone. The threesome that remained were very busy. They had occupied themselves by watching the steady procession of hunters buying licences. They observed the negotiations between the hunters and the guides. They watched as the groups left the office to begin their quest for the moose which were behind every tree. The threesome had been busy doing everything except reading the literature I had given them.

"It's lunchtime, gentlemen. Have you decided what you want to do yet?" I asked the trio.

"We haven't quite decided yet," replied the mouthpiece.

"Do you have any questions at all?" I asked.

"No, not yet anyway," he smiled.

"Okay then, we're closing for lunch and will open again at one o'clock. We can get you going then if you're ready," I said, and ushered them out the door.

When I returned at one o'clock the three were back at the door. There were more hunters, but the threesome were the first in line, and behind them were the remaining Class 'B' guides.

"Well, gentlemen, have you got it figured out yet?" I inquired as I unlocked the door.

"We're still working on it," responded the mouthpiece as he looked at the remaining guides.

"Are you sure I can't help you with anything?" I offered. "You know, I'm just a wealth of knowledge on this subject. Why, I'm so good that many of your countrymen go out of their way to seek my advice. Seven days a week they arrive at my house. Why, they even pound on my door in the wee hours of the morning or honour me with a phone call."

"No, that's fine. We just about got it figured out. You go ahead and get the rest of these boys licensed up. We'll be fine," he answered. Once more he turned his attention to everything around him and ignored the information package.

It was about three in the afternoon when the last guide was taken. "Are there any more guides hidden out somewhere?" I asked the young Metis guide who was leaving with a group of hunters.

"I don't think so. I think I'm the last one," he said.

At that point I noticed that the mouthpiece for the threesome was standing next in line at the counter.

"Well, gentlemen," I said. "Are we ready to do some business, or do you have any questions?"

"We're fine," he replied and gave me a big smile. "We've got it all figured out now. We'll take three of them Special Moose Licences, and since there's no more guides left, I guess we'll have to get us one of them there affidavits."

"News certainly travels fast," I said. The use of the affidavit, when all guides were working and unavailable, had been approved only a couple of days before. It was in response to the large number of Special Moose Licence hunters and the shortage of licensed guides.

"I guess it does at that," he said, still smiling happily.

"And what a surprise," I replied sarcastically.

"What's that?" he asked in all innocence, the smile fading.

"That you figured that out just when the last guide was taken," I said.

He didn't blink an eye, but the smile returned as he pulled his wallet from a hip pocket. He sorted through some cards before selecting his driver's licence and laid it on the counter. After watching licences being sold for the past six hours, he knew the drill real well.

"Okay," I said. "Let's get the licences out of the way, then we'll get to the affidavits."

"That sounds fair," he responded, nodding his head in agreement.

I was just starting to issue the last licence when there was a commotion at the door. We all stopped and looked, just in time to see a woman stumble through the office door. I took a second look — yes, it was a woman, a very inebriated woman. She was having a difficult time negotiating the distance from the door to the counter. With a sudden surge, she lurched past the threesome and grabbed for the counter to steady herself. It took her a few minutes to get organized, but as soon as she got a good hold on the counter, she leaned forward. It was a steadying tactic to keep from falling.

The threesome had stepped back to avoid contact. They looked first at her, then at me. One could not miss the looks; the trio were thoroughly amused. Obviously they had not yet had the pleasure of being introduced to one of Hinton's more colourful characters.

"Hi Bob," she slurred. She tried to raise a hand in

greeting, but came dangerously close to losing her balance.

"Emma," I replied, "and how are you today?" It was a redundant question, for if one thing was obvious, it was her condition.

"Bob, I just want to let you know, if anyone needshaa guide, I'm avvvaillllable," she said, and smiled. Then she tried to straighten up a bit, thought better of it, and slumped on the counter again. "Yesshh shirrreee, I'm avvvailllllable," she mumbled.

Now it was my turn to smile. I looked at the threesome who had played their cards so expertly all day. There were no smiles now, and the look of amusement that had lit up their faces was gone, as was their colour. I was looking at three of the palest faces I had ever seen. Then, reality started to set in as they realized what was transpiring. Oh yes, I could plainly see the new look. It was terror, and it was growing. They stood there numb, staring first at the woman and then at me. Not a word escaped from their lips.

"Gentlemen," I said, giving them my biggest, brightest smile, "meet Emma. She's a Class 'A' Guide." I stood watching them with all the satisfaction of someone who has just witnessed justice being meted out in the finest tradition. I paused to let this bit of information sink in and take full effect. It was working wonders. There they stood, three very self-confident men looking at Emma in total disbelief. There was no doubt in my mind that they were thunderstruck, unable to speak as they stared at the object of their good fortune. This was not a bad dream, it was a nightmare.

Finally, I broke the ice for them. "I guess you won't be needing 'them there affidavits' after all, will you, gentlemen?" I chuckled. "Why don't I just finish issuing you fellas your licences. I can tell that you're just dying to be on your way. You probably want to spend some time getting to know your guide a little better."

The mouthpiece looked at me, at Emma, then back at me.

"Ah c'mon, buddy, have a heart," he pleaded. His voice had suddenly lost all of its confidence; his take-charge attitude was withering rapidly. It looked suspiciously as if he was going to cry.

"Well, gentlemen, it's pretty obvious to me that you know the rules as well as I do. And the rules is the rules, right? Emma is a Class 'A' guide. Not only is she available, but she is also a very good guide. You have probably done better than anybody today — she is one of the best. If you refuse to hire her and someone else comes in and takes her, you still don't get the affidavit. The choice is yours," I chuckled.

"Oh, man," he whined. "Please, please have a heart. We've driven a long ways. Don't do this to us."

"Sorry, guys," I replied. "Them's the rules. You've also spent the whole day sitting here and watching guide after guide being hired. You were first in line this morning and again this afternoon — you could have had your choice of any of them. Like I said, Emma is a Class 'A' guide and a darn good one at that. Emma's not always available on such short notice. Why, I'd say this is your lucky day."

While we were talking, Emma had been hanging on

to the counter. Now she was trying to turn around without falling. She was trying, but hadn't succeeded as yet; there was not much to hang on to on that polished countertop. Finally she got a hand on the arm of the mouthpiece. The look on his face was priceless. Instinctively, he recoiled in a frantic effort to save his arm, but Emma was strong and she had a good grip. However, his actions helped to swing her around. She remained on her feet. She wobbled a bit before she got herself squared away, then she leaned back slightly and smiled at her clients. They just stood there and stared.

Suddenly, without warning, Emma raised her arm and swung it toward the street. The mouthpiece ducked just in time to avoid a solid backhand, and Emma spoke.

"When you hire me, youse also gets my man," she blurted out in a very slurred voice.

We all looked towards the door. Nobody was there, nor was anyone out on the landing. At first glance it appeared that there was no one on the steps, but on walking to the window and looking more closely, we discovered that there was indeed a second person. We all stood at the window looking down at the bottom of the steps. The man to whom Emma had referred was at the bottom of the steps, down on all fours. He was on his hands and knees, giving his all, trying to negotiate the half-dozen steps to the landing. That first step was proving to be quite a problem, but he was a determined cuss. He did not give up.

"Can your man walk?" I asked Emma. "Or has he just had one too many?" I watched as the crawler tried

71

to figure out which limb to move next. The decision took too long and he crumbled to the ground in a heap.

"He looks like a gamer, doesn't he?" I said for the hunters' benefit. "Notice the determination? See how he tries to get right up again each time he falls?"

"He'll be just fine soon's we gits to the bush," Emma mumbled in defence of her man.

Finally I was able to get the stunned threesome back to the counter. I finished issuing the licences and collecting the funds.

"There you go, gentlemen," I said as I handed out the last licence. "Where you going to take your clients?" I asked Emma.

"To the Berland," she slurred again.

"Where on the Berland?" I asked. "Now don't go getting too far off the beaten track. I plan on stopping by one day, and you know I don't have a 4x4 so I can't get in there too far," I reminded her.

"Campground, east of the bridge," she muttered. "Coffee always on. You be sure to stop in fer a coffee."

"Good, I can get in there. Well, gentlemen!" I smiled again at the threesome standing there in stunned silence. "Don't be too harsh and prejudge this lady," I cautioned them. "She's been guiding in this country for many years. Oh yes — I've never eaten her cooking, but rumour has it that she is also one of the best camp cooks in the country. You watch, she'll surprise you. Now, y'all enjoy your hunt."

They left the office: Two of them helped peel Emma off the counter and negotiate the door and steps. At the bottom of the steps her man was still trying to get a hand, or a foot, or both, on the first step. They paused long enough to collect him as well, and then headed for their vehicle.

Three days later, when I was patrolling the Berland area, I thought I'd stop and say hello to Emma and her clients. As I pulled into the campground, I noticed three bull moose hanging in the trees. It looked to me as if it had been a pretty successful hunt. One of the hunters, the mouthpiece, was outside the tent in the campground when I stopped my car. As I stepped out, he stumbled over to me and put his arm around my shoulder.

"It looks like you've had a successful hunt," I said.

"Best hunt I ever bin on," he slurred, taking a hefty slug of — well, it might have been coffee. "An' we got the best guide in th' whole worl' too. Yesssirrreee. The best guide in the whole worl'. An' guess what, buddy, we booked her for next year awreddy. So, whaddya think of that, huh?" he garbled, and reached for a tree to steady himself.

"I think you lucked out," I replied. "I think you lucked out."

"A BEAR KILLED MY WIFE!"

It was shortly after midnight when the phone rang. It seemed as if I had gone to bed hours ago, and yet it had only been a few minutes. In a groggy state I groped my way out of the bedroom and promptly stumbled over a sawhorse, then for good measure kicked a can of paint.

My house was only half-built . . . well, not quite half. Not counting unpainted walls and bare floors, the kitchen, the master bedroom, and the small bathroom where the girls slept were almost complete — the rest of the house was a construction zone. Boards, drywall, batts of insulation, paint cans, and tools of all sorts lay

74

scattered across the floors. The place was a disaster area, a hazard at any time of the day, but at night, in the dark, it was a nightmare.

"Do you know what time it is?" I asked when I picked up the receiver.

"My wife . . .!" screamed a voice. It was high-pitched, but I figured it sounded like a male voice, albeit an hysterical male voice. My and wife were the only words I understood, although they were followed by a barrage of words coming so fast that I couldn't catch another thing he jabbered. My first thought was that it was another call from the midnight shift down at the mill. Lately, some of the boys had taken to calling me in the wee hours of the morning to settle some minuscule argument they were having. My first instinct was to hang up, but for some unknown reason I stayed with it.

"Slow down!" I yelled into the receiver. "Calm down, man, speak slower, I can't understand a word you're saying, but if you're looking for your wife, she's not here."

"My wife!" he screeched again and then started to cry. "She's dead . . ."

Now I was awake. Not even the boys at the mill would pull a stunt like this.

"You should call the police," I informed him. "I'm the game warden. Deaths are not my responsibility. You have to report it to the police."

"She was killed . . ." howled the distressed man, and again he screamed and jabbered away so fast I couldn't get the rest. To say the poor guy was excited would be an understatement—the man was hysterical. By now, I was wide awake. It took several minutes of coaxing, but I finally got him settled.

"I'm sorry," I said, "this is really a matter for the police, but if you'll give me the information, I'll pass it along for you. Now, did I hear right—did you say that someone has been killed?"

"My wife!" he wailed. "My wife's been killed! Please, you've got to help me."

"I'm trying, sir, I'm trying," I replied. "I just need a little information and I'll have the police out there in a jiffy. Who are you, sir, what's your name?" I asked, trying to sound efficient and in charge.

"She's dead . . . dead! My wife's dead, I tell you. And you want to know who I am?" he screamed at me.

"I'm sorry, sir," I apologized. "I just need to know where you are and where I can find your wife. I'm going to need the information so I can let the police know. They have to know where to come to. Now, if you could please just tell me where they can find you, then I'll handle it from there on for you."

"I-I'm at the hotel on the highway," he sobbed. "Please hurry."

"Thank you, sir, we'll be right there," I replied. Actually, I meant the police would be right there. "Now, if you can only tell me where we might find your wife, sir, that would be helpful. Is she with you?"

"No, no, she's dead—dead, I told you. A bear . . . a bear killed my wife!" he wailed.

"A what?" I asked. Now that really got my attention. The death was definitely a situation for the police, but if it was a bear, that was a whole different matter. The bear was my responsibility.

"Did you say a . . . a bear?" I asked.

"Yes, that's what I've been trying to tell you, a bear killed my wife. Please, help me!"

"Where is your wife now, sir?" I asked.

"Sh-she's at the camp," came the weak response. "She's at the camp and she's dead."

"If you'll tell me where the camp is, I can call the RCMP and we'll be on our way," I said.

"I don't know," he sobbed. "I don't know where the camp is. It's on the highway, in the hills. There's a campsite. That's all I know."

"If you can tell me which campsite, sir, that would be a big help. There are a number of campsites along the highway in this district.

"I'm sorry," he sobbed again. "I don't know, I don't know the name of it, or where it is. I don't know."

"That's okay, just tell me which direction it is from Hinton."

"It's east of town. About ten miles. I think."

"Okay, that'll help. I'll call the RCMP. We'll be right out."

"A bear," he started to sob again. "A bear attacked her in the campground and killed her. And now my poor wife, she's dead."

"Okay, sir," I said. "You wait right where you're at. I'll get the police and we'll be right there."

"I'm gonna go back to the camp, to help my wife!" He suddenly stopped crying and blurted it out.

"No, no, don't do that!" I cautioned him. Now it was my turn to get excited. We certainly didn't need two dead people on this night. "You stay right where you're at. I'll be down to the hotel in a couple of minutes and you can go back with us. I don't want you going back there alone. Leave that to us just in case the bear is still around. Do you understand?"

"I understand," he said. "I'll wait here for you."

I hung up the phone and called the RCMP. The dead lady was their problem. The bear was mine. My mind started to race like crazy. What was I going to do with my problem when I got out to the campsite?

I charged into the basement and busted open boxes and crates looking for my firearms. I found my rifle and shotgun just as my search was halted by a loud banging on the door. I raced upstairs and flung the door open.

"Do you always answer the door in the buff?" asked a somewhat startled RCMP constable.

"Sometimes . . . only when I'm pressed," I mumbled.

"Well, get your pants on, man. I just got a call about a bear killing a woman," he said.

"I guess I got the same call," I told him. "I'll be with you in a minute."

We travelled together in the RCMP cruiser; our first stop was the Hinton Hotel. The caller wasn't there. The night clerk advised us that no one had used the pay phone or the hotel phone.

"You know, I'm really gonna be ticked off if this was a call from the boys at the mill," I said as we got back into the cruiser. Actually, I knew I was gonna be relieved and was praying that it had been the boys at the mill. But we needed to check it out, so we departed for the closest campsite, that being in the Obed Hills on Highway 16.

"What do you think?" asked the constable. "Was this call legit or not?"

"I don't know," I replied. "I get a lot of stupid calls from the boys down at the mill. It seems that some of them have nothing better to do than to call me up at all hours of the night. Right now, I'd rather be looking at a prank call than a corpse. But you know, the guy sounded pretty upset on the phone." We drove on in silence.

As we approached the Obed campground I was surprised to see a car with its headlights on parked on the shoulder of the road just before the turnoff into the campsite.

"This could be legit," I said. "Look at the licence plate — this car's from Ontario." We drew up alongside of the parked car, and I motioned for the driver, an elderly man, to roll his window down.

I sensed his reluctance as he just sat there and stared back at me, not moving. I got out of the patrol car, walked over to his car, and opened the driver's door.

"Good evening, sir," I said, greeting the elderly gentleman. "My name is Bob Adams. I'm with Fish and Wildlife from Hinton. By chance, did you happen to phone me tonight?"

"I-I did," he responded, speaking very quietly. He was not nearly as excited as when he had called earlier.

"Are you okay, sir?" I asked.

The elderly gentleman looked towards the

79

campground and hesitated for a minute before turning back to me.

"My wife's dead, you know. She was killed by a bear."

"I'm sorry to hear that, sir," I said. "I'll go and have a look. It would help if you could tell me where the attack occurred.

"Just before dark," he replied in almost a whisper. "It was still light out and this bear charged out of the bush and killed my wife. It happened right in front of our tent, right in front of me," he said, and started to sob. "She's dead, right in front of our tent."

"I'm sorry, sir," I replied. "It would really help if you could recall which campsite you were in."

Suddenly I could feel my knees start to tremble at the thought of stumbling around in the dark looking for a bear that had just killed someone. I had a feeling that knowing where the attack had occurred would be a big help. Although I had no idea why.

"N-no, I don't. It . . . it was over there somewhere," he said and pointed off into the darkness.

Suddenly the night seemed to be blacker than black. This, I knew, was going to be one horrible night.

"Okay. You better stay here, sir, while we go over and check it out. As soon as we're ready, one of us will come back for you."

"I'm coming too. It's my wife over there. I want to come with you." For the first time he sounded like he might be in control.

"No! You stay right here. We'll come and get you if we need you."

80

I'm not sure whether I convinced him or whether he was relieved that he had been ordered to stay. I would have been happy to stay. In any event, the elderly gentleman turned his head towards the campground and stared off into the darkness.

"He's our man, all right," I said as I got back into the cruiser. "Apparently the attack occurred before dark. And he hasn't a clue which campsite they were at or where her body might be, other than it's in front of a tent somewhere in the campground."

"Well, you're the expert with bears," replied the Horse Cop. "What do you recommend?"

I was trying desperately to think of something brilliant to do, but kept drawing blanks.

"Well?" he asked. "What now?"

"I guess we go find us a tent with a mauled body in front of it," I replied.

We slowly drove into the campground. We noticed a light coming from a campsite near the back of the campground.

"Looks to me like there's someone else in here," I said, pointing to the light. "I don't imagine that a body would have been able to light the lantern."

"It doesn't make sense that he would have lit a lantern before he left, does it?" asked the constable.

"Not to me," I replied, "but people have been known to do some funny things under stress."

We drove slowly through the campground, checking each campsite as we came to it, and finding each one vacant. As we approached the campsite with the light, we could see a gas lantern hanging in a tree in front of

81

a tent. A person sitting in a chair, reading a book, never even bothered to look up as we drove past.

"This certainly can't be the spot," I said, gesturing to our campsite reader. "That person obviously pulled in here after dark and has no idea what happened." Personally, I was quite relieved; that had to be a good sign that the bear had left. "Let's check out the rest of the campsites and see what else we've got."

We sat in the car at the last campsite in the campground and peered off into the black of the night. There was only the campsite reader in the campground. Unless we were missing something, there was not one other campsite in use. We looked at each other, dumbfounded.

"Is that car still out by the road?" I asked, thinking that we had really been duped.

"It's still there," replied the Horse Cop. "Let's go back to the campsite with the light on and ask if they've seen or heard anything."

Arriving back at the campsite, we both got out of the car and walked towards the tent. An elderly woman, sitting in a foldaway chair, put her book down and looked up.

"Good evening," she said, greeting us with a smile. "Isn't it a lovely evening?"

"It certainly is that. In fact, it's the kind of evening that just makes a person feel good to be alive," I replied. "And how are you this fine evening?"

"I'm very good, thank you."

"If you don't mind me asking, how long have you been in the campground?" I asked.

"Since early this afternoon. Would either of you gentlemen like a coffee or something to drink?" she offered.

"No, thanks, we're on duty right now," replied my partner.

"Have you seen anybody else since you've been here?" I asked.

"I haven't seen a soul until you two gentlemen drove up just now," she replied.

"Are you alone, or is there somebody else with you?" I asked.

"No, just me and my husband. We're on holidays, you know."

"I see, and where is your husband right now?"

"Oh, I don't know," she said. "He's not here right now."

"Have you had any problems with a bear?"

"Heavens, no!" she said and laughed.

"You didn't by any chance see a bear around here this evening, did you?"

"Oh yes, we did. There was a little bear that walked out of the bush over there," she said, pointing off into the darkness to where I presumed there were trees. "He walked right through the campground and then back into the bush, but he hasn't been back."

"Are you expecting your husband to return here this evening?" Suddenly I was feeling a whole lot better about investigating this complaint.

"I certainly hope so," she responded.

"It seems to me that it's a little strange that your

husband isn't here with you. Wouldn't you say that that was a little strange?"

"I certainly would," she said crisply, "and I'm going to give him a piece of my mind when he gets back. I don't know what came over him. You know, when that little bear walked out of the bush, my husband never said a word. The next thing I knew, he had jumped into the car and was driving away. I haven't seen him since."

"Your wife's fine," I advised the elderly gentleman when we got back to the highway. "She's sitting in front of the tent, reading a book, and waiting for you."

"No, that can't be. My wife's dead," he said, and he was very coherent and sober. "She's been killed by a bear. I know it. She's not fine. She's dead."

"I think you're mistaken," I offered. "I just spoke to your wife, sir. She's very much alive and quite all right. Apparently the bear just walked through the campground. It never went near your tent at all."

"No, no," he argued. "She's dead. The bear killed her, I know it."

"According to your wife, you and the bear disappeared about the same time, sir. She hasn't seen either of you since. In fact, when we first stopped to talk to her, she was sitting in a chair, in front of the tent, reading a book. Now, that doesn't sound like a dead person to me, does it to you?"

It took a lot of convincing to get the poor fellow to agree to go back to the campsite, and even seeing his wife was not enough to convince him that she was still alive. In fact, he would not get out of his car to talk to her.

It was getting to be early morning and we were still sitting and talking to both of them. With him in his car and her by the campfire, together we watched the sun rise on what I was sure would be his last camping trip in the shadow of the Rockies.

THE POACHER

The first table in the restaurant was full, and the men sitting around it were intent as they listened to the big guy, the poacher. He was obviously holding court and they were leaning on his every word. As I walked by, he turned his attention to me.

"If you want to catch a poacher, you gotta think like a poacher," the big guy said, and the boys all looked at me and laughed.

"You're right," I replied. "I'll keep that in mind."

"And another thing," he continued, because it's best to say it all when one is on a roll. "You better get yourself some decent equipment. You're never going to catch me unless you can run with me. And you can't run far with that shiny green Pontiac you drive up and down the road." Once more his comment was met with a chorus of laughter.

"Thanks for the tip," I replied. I thought to myself that it was time to change restaurants.

Since arriving in Hinton, I often found myself to be the punchline in the poacher's jokes. The sad part of it was that he was half-right. Oh, I had no problem thinking like a poacher. As far back as I could remember, when we lived on the Stump Farm, we had lived off the land; and if I do say so myself, I had gotten pretty good at keeping the larder filled without getting caught by the local game warden. But I certainly had a problem when it came to running with the big dogs.

There was less equipment in the Hinton District than there were Fish Cops, and there was only one of those. I had my own car, my own rifle, my own shotgun. A pair of wonky binoculars was the only thing that was government issue.

There was no Ski-Doo to check hunters or trappers in the wintertime when the snow was up to a gravedigger's butt. There was no boat to check hunters or fishermen on the rivers or lakes. There was no truck, let alone a four-wheel-drive truck, to haul moose, elk, deer, bear, or bear traps, or to check hunters and fishermen in those out-of-the-way places down side roads and back in on seismic trails. There were no horses to check hunters, guides, and outfitters back in the mountains. It was safe to say, the big man was right—the Hinton district was a veritable desert when it came to equipment.

Now, the poacher sitting in the coffee shop, laughing with his buddies at my expense, had all these toys and more at his disposal. His favourite toy, one he purportedly had built himself, was a beloved swamp buggy. It was a Volkswagen mounted on oversized dual tires. The swamp buggy, I was told, could whip across a muskeg, skim sloughs and bogs, traverse rivers and streams, or float across mountain valleys covered in several feet of powdery snow — and it could perform all these feats with the carcass of a poached moose strapped across the top. Yes, the swamp buggy was all the equipment needed for the rugged terrain of a mountain district. There was no doubt, the poacher had me outgunned. He also had a reputation. One that he thoroughly enjoyed.

"One day," I promised, "one day, my friend, there will be a day of reckoning. And I've got nothing but time. Remember, they pay me to spend my time catching the likes of you." I can tell you, this was one man I had vowed to catch. Sooner or later he and I would meet, for it is indeed a long old alley that doesn't have a trash can.

"Not me," he laughed. "You'll never catch me." The dialogue was almost the same every time our paths crossed. He was a braggart. He was a boaster. He was confident.

Deep inside, I had to reluctantly admit that the chances were slim. I was having a devil of a time finding him in the bush, let alone catching him. I had checked him and his swamp buggy only once in the field. The only thing I could do on that occasion was to admire and drool over his equipment, for he and the machine were squeaky clean.

I had spent many hours listening, watching, and

researching the poacher. One thing I learned was that, although he hunted by himself, he never worked alone. There were always willing hands available to him at the end of the trail. It was a very good system and I had a pretty good idea how it worked. Then, one day I received a tip, an officer's best friend: The poacher and his swamp buggy were out stealing the Crown's beef.

It was a week before the deer season, and the poacher was out in the foothills, doing what he did best. He would be returning to Hinton sometime after dark with all his ill-gotten gains. Long before dark, long before the cutters and the haulers left the bush, I set a trap of my own. I felt confident that the talk at the coffee shop in the morning would be how the poacher had been beaten at his own game.

I chose my spot carefully, a spot where I could hide on the haul road north of Hinton. I waited and I watched. I watched several vehicles drive past. I could hear the loaded pulp trucks long before I saw them and the clouds of dust they kicked up as they ground their way towards Hinton with their heavy loads of spruce and pine trees. I saw the same trucks return, empty, kicking up more dust as they roared back up the road, at breakneck speed, for another load. To them, time was money. Near the end of the day, I watched the buses hauling cutters out of the bush. They too drove at a good clip, wasting no time, and they threw up just as much dust. An assortment of small trucks — half-tons, three-quarter-tons, most of them four-wheel-drive and most of them owned by the mill — shot past, dodging the logging trucks and the buses as they wove their way through the clouds of dust. All that long afternoon I watched the dust drift to the east and slowly settle over the countryside, and over me. My green Pontiac, long since covered with a thick layer of dust, was the same colour as the surrounding trees, the colour of dirt. My car was almost invisible. Now my trap was complete.

After the buses left the forest, activity on the road almost ceased. The forest took on an eerie silence. I watched and I waited for the one vehicle that I was sure would be carrying the poacher and the illegal animal.

The sun was fading in the west and the Rocky Mountains were casting long shadows over the foothills when, in the distance, I heard a vehicle. It was coming from town. I watched as it moved slowly along the road. A three-quarter-ton 4x4 crept into sight. It wasn't moving fast enough to raise a grain of dust. The driver was carefully scanning both sides of the road as he moved past me. I knew immediately that the tip had been a good one. I smiled to myself as the lookout drove out of sight. Somewhere back in the hills was another truck. It would be the one with the poacher and an illegal animal in it.

"Yes!" I whispered. "Today, my friend. Today is the day."

Suddenly, out of nowhere, another truck appeared. A half-ton whistled past me in a cloud of dust, heading for town. Suddenly I was on the edge of my seat, every muscle in my body tensed for action.

"There he goes!" yelled the little guy in my head. "Get him before he gets away."

Instinctively I reached for the keys that for the last

seven hours had hung lifeless in the ignition. I almost turned them. Oh man, the temptation to give chase was great, but I didn't bite. I held my ground. The guy was in a hurry to get somewhere. He was not my guy. Then, before the dust had settled, another vehicle whistled past like a shot. Did one of these babies have an animal in it? I doubt it, I thought, as I tried to relax. For some reason it didn't seem to fit the plan.

I waited a long time before I spotted a three-quarter-ton 4x4 creeping slowly back down the road. Ha, I thought, the culprit returns. Before it arrived, another half-ton roared past. For a second I lost the first in the dust cloud, but I made my move. I turned the keys, the engine jumped to life, and I sprang the trap. The poor driver couldn't believe his eyes when he saw the green Pontiac burst out of the forest, through the cloud of dust. The look on his face said it all. I was his worst nightmare.

I couldn't believe my eyes either, because my carefully laid trap had caught one of the mill workers, driving a mill truck.

"Good afternoon, sir," I greeted him. "This is a game check. You wouldn't happen to be carrying any wildlife, would you?"

"Yes," he blurted out nervously. "I mean, no. No, I haven't. I mean . . ."

I looked into the back of the truck, not expecting to see anything, and received another surprise.

"Well now, what do we have here?" I said, uncovering the carcass of a deer. "Is this yours?"

"Yes . . . I mean, it's not mine," he quickly protested,

"I didn't shoot it. Look, I don't even have a gun."

"Would you care to tell me who shot the animal?" I asked.

"I don't know. I can't," he replied.

"You don't know, or you can't?" I asked again.

"I-I can't," he replied, and hung his head.

"That's your prerogative, sir," I replied, realizing that the poacher had won again. Somewhere, he and his swamp buggy were roaming free. "You, however, will be charged with illegal possession of wildlife."

"Will I lose my hunting licence?" he asked.

"Oh, you betcha," I replied. "For one whole year from the date of your conviction. Now, if this isn't your deer, and I believe you when you say it's not, we both know who it belongs to, don't we? Do you think it was worth it?"

He sat in silence and hung his head as I issued the ticket to appear in court. He never left his vehicle when I removed the illegal deer from the back of his truck. For me, however, it was a shallow victory because, sadly, he was not the man I was looking for.

"Well, maybe if it doesn't violate the sacred trust, you can tell me one thing. Is my poachin' buddy still out here?" I asked.

"No," replied the sad man, shaking his head. "I saw him this afternoon i-in the Hinton Hotel bar."

"Did he ask you to pick up this deer for him?" The victim just shook his head. I could already hear the laughing and the banter that would be making the rounds at the coffee shop. Once more I would be the butt of the jokes.

The next morning, I was standing at the counter in my office when, to my surprise, the truck I had taken the illegal deer out of the night before pulled up and stopped. I had an unexpected visitor. It was an old family friend, a man I had known since I was a child on the Stump Farm, who climbed out of the truck and confidently walked into my office. He greeted me, well, just like you would expect an old family friend to greet you. Since leaving Edson, he had done very well for himself and had become a supervisor at the mill. Maybe this would be the lucky break I needed to get the poacher.

"Bobby, how are you?" he said as he greeted me and shook my hand warmly, just what one would expect of an old friend. "I should have stopped by sooner, but a person gets busy, you know how it is."

"I sure do," I replied. "I don't think I've really had the time to stop and see anybody myself since I've been in Hinton."

"Bobby," he said. He called me Bobby, just like my mother used to. "Bobby, I need a favour from you."

"Name it," I replied. "I'm always happy to help an old friend."

"Bobby, I understand you picked up one of my men with a deer last night."

"Well, I picked up a man with a deer all right, but I didn't know he was one of your men," I replied.

"He is, Bobby, he's an honest, hard-working man. He wouldn't hurt a flea. You know what I mean. He's one of my best men," he said. "I want to assure you,

93

Bobby, that this was all a mistake. He didn't shoot that animal, you know."

"So he said," I replied.

"You see, Bobby, he was only . . . well, he was only trying to help a friend. And you know how things happen sometimes, people get themselves in trouble when they try to help."

"I do. It's sorta like, you get caught and the friend walks," I replied.

"Exactly," said the old family friend. "I knew you'd understand."

"Absolutely," I replied. "And I'm glad you've talked some sense into this honest, hard-working man. When is he gonna come in and tell me the name of the poacher who actually shot the animal?"

"No! That's not what I mean," he quickly blurted out. "I was hoping that you might see your way clear to help out . . ."

"Oh, okay, you mean . . . now I think I know what you mean," I said to him, and nodded my head to assure him.

"I knew I could count on you," he replied and I could hear the relief in his voice as he relaxed.

Then I leaned over the counter real close to him and whispered. "By the way, old friend, you know, I did make a mistake last night when I seized that deer. I think I should make amends now, don't you?"

"Am I ever happy to hear you say that. You'll drop the charges then, won't you, Bobby?"

"First, let me tell you what I'm going to do," I said. I looked him straight in the eye and smiled. "You know, my friend, that truck you're driving is the same company truck the deer was in last night, and I'm betting there's still blood and hair in the truck box. Like I said, I probably made a small mistake when I didn't seize it as evidence last night, so I want to thank you for personally delivering it to me today."

The old family friend just stared at me with his mouth open, as if he had just been hit between the eyes with a hammer. He couldn't believe what he had just heard.

"Y-you would too, wouldn't you, you . . ." he suddenly blurted out and stuttered trying to find the right word to describe me. Old friendships obviously didn't die hard with him.

"It would be my pleasure," I smiled. "And if it's not gone in ten seconds, it's mine."

The old family friend just about tore the door off the wall getting out of my office. Gravel sprayed the front of the building as he spun the wheels in his haste to get away.

The next morning I avoided the restaurant, but I couldn't avoid the poacher.

"I understand you had a little excitement in the last twenty-four hours," chuckled the poacher when I met him on the street later that morning.

"Not really," I replied. "It was just business as usual."

"My sources tell me you got the wrong man," he said.

"Oh no, I got the right man," I replied.

"How do you figure that?" he asked.

"Well, let's see, if I remember correctly, I got an illegal deer and I got the guy who had it in his possession. Unless you know something I don't, that you wish to share with me, I'd say I got the right guy."

"Well, my friend. You're just gonna have to get up a little earlier in the morning if you want the right guy!" He laughed and walked away.

A few weeks later, late on a Saturday night, I was working a roadblock north of Hinton on the Forestry Trunk Road, at its junction with the road to the Lower Hay River area and the Berland River. There was a lot of traffic, even for a Saturday night. Most of the traffic was generated by the massive construction work servicing the new town of Grande Cache, the mine, the new railway, and the highway. But every now and then a hunter drove through. About two-thirty in the morning one of the hunters was the poacher himself.

"You're still here?" he asked. There was no mistaking the surprised tone in his voice.

"What do you think, is this early enough to catch the real poachers?" I asked.

"Not this time," he replied. "But it's a hell of a try. You're getting closer."

I checked him and his truck from one end to the other. But he was squeaky clean. In fact, he and his truck were as clean as I'd ever seen them. Not only was there no animal, but there was not a hair, not even a drop of blood in this poacher's vehicle. Why, there wasn't even any dust or snow on the truck or in the box. It was clean as a whistle.

"If I didn't know better, I'd say that you had just washed this thing."

"You know I always keep a clean vehicle," he chuckled. "By the way, you should do yourself a favour and go home and get some sleep. There's nothing coming out tonight."

I stayed for a couple of hours after my friend the poacher had left, but I knew and he knew that there would be nothing illegal moved out on this night. I went home and went to bed.

I had barely got to sleep when the call came. It was anonymous.

"If you're up to a drive this morning, you may want to check out the seismic line about eight miles out on the Lower Hay River Road. Check out a stand of spruce trees about a hundred yards west of the road," said a disguised voice.

"Would you like to come with me?" I asked. "I'm not sure where that is."

"Sure you do," the voice replied and then laughed. "It's eight miles from where you were set up last night. It'll be easy for you — you'll even be able to drive that game warden car of yours right up to the spot." Then the phone went dead.

I hadn't planned on a trip into that area, but right after a quick breakfast I was on my way north again. Exactly eight miles from the previous evening's roadblock, I found the new seismic line. It ran straight west from the road. And judging from the well-packed tracks, there had been a lot of traffic on it since the last snowfall. About a hundred yards off the road, the seismic line ran right through the middle of a heavy stand of spruce. I stopped my game warden car and got out. A single trail led to the north, winding back through the trees for about fifty yards.

And there they were, laid out in the snow around the base of the trees. All neatly trimmed, wrapped in cheesecloth, and frozen solid, eight quarters of moose meat. They were waiting for their trip to the meat market.

On Monday morning I went looking for the poacher. I couldn't prove he had shot the animals, but both he and I knew that he was responsible. I found him sitting in a booth having coffee with his friends.

"Hey, Bob," he called when I walked in. "I heard you had some excitement after I left you." His friends didn't laugh, but the looks on their faces said it all—they were enjoying this. There would be laughs aplenty when I rose to the bait and when I left.

But I never said a word. I walked over to his booth, and without waiting for an invite, I plunked myself down right next to him. Then I slid over and sealed him in, nice and tight. He wasn't going anywhere until I let him out.

"Why don't you sit down and take a load off your feet?" he laughed. His friends laughed too. Was my inability to catch this nimrod to be their constant source of enjoyment?

Then, for all to see, I took out a ticket book. Now this was not just any old ticket book. This was a brand-new one. There was not a mark on it. It was as clean as a whistle, just like his truck had been early Sunday morning. The laughter died instantly and was replaced by looks of amused interest. His friends wouldn't have missed this moment for the world. You could have heard a pin drop as I slowly opened the cover and revealed the first ticket.

"Wait a minute," said the poacher breaking the silence. "What's this? What do you think you're doing?"

"Oh, I think you know what this is," I replied, giving him my nicest smile. Slowly I pulled the pen from my shirt pocket.

"Hey, just a minute, you got nothin' on me," the poacher whined. "You can't prove nothin'."

"Look," I said and smiled at him, "it's nice and clean. And it's just for you, my friend."

"C'mon, now," he said. "You can't give me no ticket. You got nothin' on me."

"You see, my friend," I continued, ignoring his pleas, "right here at the top of the page, on the first line, that's where your name goes. Now, I prefer to have the last name first, but it really doesn't matter. It can go either way." Very carefully and neatly, I printed his name in big block letters.

Now, for the first time since I had known him, the poacher was really starting to squirm. I think he would have left if he could have figured out a way to get past me, but he was stuck in that booth for as long as I wanted him there. His friends, on the other hand, they could have left at any time, but they weren't about to leave and miss this little show. Their eyes were wide open. This was going to be a story worth telling. They, too, were enjoying themselves.

"Now, your address goes on the second line here, and you have to include your phone number and your vital statistics," I said, and pointed out the place on the ticket where each should go.

"Hey, look now, I'm not taking that ticket," he squealed. His voice had risen three octaves since the last time he had spoken. He pushed as far as he could get into the back of the booth and held up his hands, palms out. "You got nothin' on me. I'm clean."

"Now, down here on these lines," I continued and moved a little closer to him. "This is the body of the ticket, it's where we put the offence that you've committed. If you happen to have been lucky and say, ended up with . . . oh, say something like eight quarters of meat all neatly done up in cheesecloth, that can be recorded as 'illegal possession of wildlife, to wit: eight quarters of the Queen's beef'. Now that's the main charge, but the neat thing about our ticket is that it can be the seizure receipt as well. There's no need to write out a second receipt."

"No way," he protested. "Let me outta here. You got nothin' on me. I don't know a thing about those eight quarters of moose!"

"MOOSE!" I repeated, and sat back and stared at him for a long second.

"Yeah, moose," he declared.

"Did I say anything about moose?" I asked the boys sitting around the table.

"No," came a chorus of replies.

"I didn't mention moose," I said to the poacher, who was now visibly shaken. "But you know, you're right.

Those eight quarters were moose, all right."

"I don't believe it!" one of the boys exclaimed.

"Well, I'll be! He's got ya!" another chimed in. "You know, if I hadn't been sitting here, I wouldn't have believed it, but he's done it — he's got ya cold."

"Now, court dates in Hinton are on Mondays at two o'clock in the afternoon," I said, continuing as if this was an ordinary, everyday occurrence. "I normally let an individual pick his own court date. So, my friend, you can pick any Monday you'd like to appear in Hinton, or if you'd like to plead guilty, we can have the case waived to a location of your choice," I said. Then I pushed the brand-new ticket book over in front of him and ordered a coffee.

He sat as far back as he could get in the seat, away from the ticket book, and stared at that book for several minutes. His friends sat there with the dumbest grins on their faces that one person ever told another about. Everyone but the poacher was enjoying this.

"So, what do you think?" I asked. "Do you think you can handle that?"

"H-handle w-what?" he stammered, never taking his eyes off that ticket. Oh, this wait had been worth it.

"Oh, I just about forgot the bluey," I said.

"Bluey! What's the bluey?" he asked. The poacher looked stunned as he tried to come to grips with what was happening.

"That's the second copy of the ticket. It's your copy."

"M-my copy? W-what's going on? What do you think you're d-doing anyway?"

"I'm just helping you out," I said in as serious a tone

101

as I could manage. Then I tapped the ticket book. Actually, I had heard that one of my cohorts in southern Alberta had been taking quite a ribbing about his inability to catch one of the local poachers. This was a method that he had devised, and I had been waiting for the right time to use it. This was the right time.

"You see, this book, my friend, this book is for you. Except for the first ticket, which I'll take, the rest of the book is of unissued tickets, they're all for you. It's a gift from me."

"For me?" he replied quickly. "What do you mean, for me? I don't want it."

"Sure you do," I replied. "This is my busy season. And you know better than anyone that I don't have either the time or the equipment to chase after you. I figure if you have a ticket book, the next time you do something wrong, you can just fill in the blanks, just like I showed you. You keep the bluey and make sure I get the rest. You can drop them off at my office whenever it's convenient."

I finished my coffee and got up to leave. Then I turned back and dropped a dime on the table. "Oh, by the way, I always pay for my own coffee."

As I left the coffee shop, the howls of laughter from the poacher's friends echoed throughout the coffee shop and rolled out into the street.

Ah yes, I thought, it is good to get the last laugh.

THE BEADED
MOOSEHIDE JACKET

"Ah, yes!" I said as I closed my eyes and took a deep breath. There was a new aroma in the Hinton air. And it wasn't the grab-your-throat, choke-you-till-you-throw-up type that spewed from the mill. This was an aroma that tickled my nostrils and brought a flood of memories from the past. It was an aroma that I would never forget. It grabbed me and transported me back to another time, to another place. For a moment I was a young boy again, living on the Stump Farm with a deep passion for a pair of genuine moosehide moccasins. The memory that flashed through my mind was of the winter day when I traded my squirrel pelts for the pair of moccasins. I loved those genuine moosehide moccasins more than any piece of clothing I ever owned.

I was standing on the steps of the Fish and Wildlife Office in Hinton, and the aroma was strong, as if the source was right beside me. I hastened to the side of the building just in time to catch sight of a man walking into the back door of the Hinton Hotel bar. There was nothing about the man that was special—it was the jacket he was wearing. My eyes were drawn to it immediately.

It was not uncommon to see clothing of all descriptions in the booming town of Hinton in the mid-sixties. There were people of every description and there were people from every walk of life—miners, construction workers, engineers, labourers, government personnel. It seemed as though everyone had converged on Hinton. Some were looking to make their fortune, others were just thankful for the chance of a job and a paycheque. Yes, there were hordes of transient workers, and they dressed in a wide assortment of outerwear.

But that jacket was unique. It was handmade out of moosehide, and a colourful beaded pattern adorned the front and back. It was absolutely stunning. And it had the same distinctive aroma as my genuine moosehide moccasins.

A couple of days later, I was sitting in my office when I heard the door open. Before the door had closed, and before I saw the person who entered, I got a whiff of the familiar scent. Yes, on a rush of air the distinctive aroma of genuine Indian-tanned moosehide had just entered the Hinton Fish and Wildlife Office. There was not just a trace of the aroma—it was the real thing, strong and hearty.

"Good day, my friend," I said, as I charged out of my private office and hastened to the counter to greet the man who stood there. I could not hide my enthusiasm for the genuine Indian-tanned moosehide jacket that he was wearing.

"Hi," he replied, and gave me a funny sort of look.

"Man, that is certainly one nice-looking jacket you got there." It could have been the one I had seen earlier,

I couldn't be sure; but it was definitely the source of the distinctive aroma.

"Yeah, it's not bad," he replied, looking down at the front. Unconsciously, he ran his hands over the front of the jacket, letting his fingers gently caress the tightly sewn beads.

"Do you mind if I have a good look at it?" I asked. "I've been known to have a weakness for this type of handicraft."

"Not at all," he smiled. First he turned around so that I could get a good look at the full jacket. Then he took it off and laid it on the counter. He never knew how close he came to losing the jacket at that point.

Fringes, about three inches long, dangled the length of the sleeves from the shoulders to both cuffs. There were fringes across the shoulders, on the back of the jacket, and across the chest. There were fringes dangling at the bottom of the jacket. The width of each was so even they looked as if they had been machine-cut.

But what really caught my eye was the beadwork — it took my breath away. There were literally thousands of tiny, multicoloured beads. Each one had been hand-sewn onto the buckskin, and they had been sewn into very intricate designs. Brilliantly coloured flowers and leaves adorned both the front and the back of the jacket. It was a masterpiece, with its own distinctive character.

"I imagine that something like this must have taken someone a lifetime to make," I said, as I carefully touched the beadwork with the tips of my fingers.

"There's this old Indian lady up in the Grande Cache country that makes them," he informed me.

"Really," I replied. "But it's got to take forever to hand-make something like this."

"I don't think so," he said, shaking his head. "If you ask me, I'd say that she's making a killing off these jackets. She seems to be able to whip one out in no time at all. I think she's got a pretty nice little thing going for herself."

"You're kidding me. Who's that?"

"I'm not sure," he said, and a frown crossed his face while he racked his brain. "It's Annie . . . or Mary . . .or something like that."

"Well, that narrows it down for me," I said. I knew several ladies up there who had the name of Annie or Mary or something like that.

"You know, the more I think about it, the more I think her name is Annie," he said, and nodded his head up and down. "Yeah, it's Annie, I'd swear to it."

"Well, how about that. Annie. Hey, you know, I think I know who you mean," I replied. At least, the number of ladies that it could be had been reduced. "So, Annie's making moosehide jackets and I didn't know about it. I think I'll just stop and have a little chat with her. I could sure use a jacket like that. Tell me, if you don't mind me asking, how much is she charging for one?"

"Only one hundred and twenty-five smackeroos," he crowed. "That's what I paid for this one and I think I got a steal."

"A-a hundred and twenty-five bucks?" I whistled. I

jerked my hand off the jacket as if it had suddenly become too hot to handle. A hundred and twenty-five bucks, that was a whole month's pay for me.

"Not bad, huh?" he said. "But I wouldn't get too set on getting one, she's a little touchy about who she sells to." Then he lifted the jacket off the counter and calmly pulled it on.

"I'll remember that," I said, almost choking on the words. "Man, I think that's a lot of money, even for a genuine Indian-tanned moosehide jacket," I mumbled.

"Not really," he commented casually. "There's a lot of money to be made in this country these days. That is, if you want to get out and work for it."

I recognized the shot: government people really don't work. The small talk came to a sudden screeching halt. The pleasantries were over. One insult per day was the quota. Friends might get two, but certainly not a stranger.

On my next trip to Grande Cache, I arranged my list of priorities. Annie's name was right at the top of my list. I felt it was my business to find out where she was getting all these moose hides that she was making a killing from. However, more importantly, I was starting to get a strong hankering for the aroma of genuine Indian-tanned buckskin and, of course, for a beaded moosehide jacket that I could call my own.

"Man," I chuckled to myself, as I drove into the Grande Cache area. "Won't Mar ever be surprised when I show up at the house with one of those jackets."

I stopped at a few houses and asked lots of questions. It appeared that there was more than one

107

Indian lady who made moosehide jackets in the Grande Cache area. I chased around and finally ended up at Annie's house. I was met by an elderly lady who, although she said her name was not Annie, seemed to be quite comfortable with me calling her Annie.

"Hello, Ranger," Annie said, greeting me out in front of the old log cabin.

"No, Annie," I replied, "I'm the game warden, I'm not a ranger. Remember Annie, rangers work for Forestry and they drive green government trucks. I work for Fish and Wildlife and drive my own car."

"Your car's green, too," she said.

"Well, that's right, Annie," I replied, "but I drive a car. Rangers drive trucks."

"Okay, Ranger, I remember," she said. There were no game wardens in Annie's life, only rangers. I was and forever would be "Ranger" to Annie.

"Would you like some tea, Ranger?" she offered.

"That sounds good, Annie," I replied to the elderly lady. "Tell me, how have you been keeping?"

"I'm okay," she replied, nodding her head. "I'm okay, but what about you? What do you want?"

"Oh, I just stopped by to see how you were doing and maybe talk to you for awhile," I replied and smiled at her.

She looked at me for a long time before she answered. "I don't think you just come to talk to me," she said cautiously.

"No, you're right, Annie," I chuckled at the old gal's foresight. "Actually, I was told that you make a pretty nice moosehide jacket. So, I thought I'd stop by and talk to you about those jackets. Maybe I could even have a look at one?"

"You wasted your time, Ranger. I got no moosehide jacket," she answered flatly.

"You know, Annie," I said, "I've been seeing more and more of the jackets. There's a number of people wearing them, and they all tell me that they're handmade and that Annie makes them. They sure are good-looking jackets," I stated.

"I got no moosehide jacket," she replied again.

"The way I see it, Annie, there's nothing wrong with selling moosehide jackets, just so long as the moose were legally taken and the hides tanned. You can sell all the jackets you want to. I thought maybe you might just have a jacket that I could try on. If you had one that fit me, I was sorta wondering how much you'd charge me for it. That's all." I tried to allay her fears.

"I don't got no moosehide jacket," she said rather firmly.

"Well, Annie, let's say if you did have a moosehide, how much would you charge me to make a moosehide jacket with the fringes and beadwork on it?"

"I got no moosehide either, Ranger," she deadpanned me.

"Well, you know, Annie," I replied slowly, "maybe I could help you. Now, I shoot a moose every fall and I usually just throw the hide away. How much would you charge me to make a jacket if I were to give you the hide?"

"Then maybe I could make you a jacket," she said. Finally we were communicating.

"That's good," I said, quite happy with the progress we were starting to make. I could already feel the jacket on my back. "So, Annie, how much would you charge me to make the jacket?"

"I don't know. How much would you give me?"

"I don't know. I'm told you're charging one hundred and twenty-five dollars, but since I'm providing the hide, maybe I could get a discount. What do you think?"

"Okay," she jumped in without a second's hesitation. "I charge you one hundred and twenty-five dollars too." I could feel the jacket slipping from my back.

"But Annie," I protested, "I'm going to give you the moosehide. You're going to be using my moosehide. Don't I get some kind of a break? I work for the government and don't make nearly as much money as these construction workers around here do."

"That's okay, Ranger," and she smiled at me, "one hundred and twenty-five dollars is okay."

"Maybe I could get you some extra moose hides. I know a lot of people who hunt moose, and most of them just throw the hides away. If that would help you out, maybe you could help me out and give me a little break on the price? What do you think, Annie? Would that be fair?"

Annie thought about the offer for awhile. "If you can get me some moose hides, then I'll make you a special jacket," she replied.

"You've got yourself a deal, Annie," I said. I could feel the jacket settling over my shoulders once again.

"I'll get you the hides, I promise."

That fall I put the word out. If anyone who shot a moose didn't want the hide, I'd be only too happy to assist them and take it off their hands. I'd even pick it up.

By the end of the hunting season, I had delivered a dozen or more moose hides to Annie. I had a feeling that it was just a matter of time before I picked up my buckskin jacket. I could already feel the softness of the buckskin and smell the distinctive aroma. It had been a long time since I had worn genuine Indian moosehide clothing. Man, would I ever surprise some folks. I could just imagine the look on Mom's face when I walked into her house wearing a genuine Indian jacket. I'll bet the Powers That Be would have a fit if I walked into head office wearing it. I didn't even have the jacket and already I was enjoying it.

As the winter progressed, more and more moosehide jackets with the perfectly cut fringes and the kaleidoscope of beadwork began to show up. I saw them in Hinton. I saw them in Grande Cache. I saw them on the road. Judging by the increasing number of jackets on the street, I ventured to guess that Annie's genuine Indian-tanned moosehide jacket factory must be in full production.

At several houses I had seen moose hides stretched on a poplar sapling frame over a smudge fire, although I had never seen anyone working on one. Come to think of it, I had never seen any sign of moose hides being tanned at Annie's, or of jackets being made, or of beads being sewn on. But the jackets still kept coming.

111

Every trip I took into Grande Cache, I made a point of stopping by Annie's and having a cup of tea with her. Each time, I would anticipate that this time my jacket would be ready. But each visit would be the same.

"Hello, Ranger!" She would greet me like an old friend.

"Hi, Annie, is my jacket ready yet?" I would always ask the same question.

"Not yet, Ranger," Annie would reply with a big sly smile. "Not yet."

"H-how long will it be, Annie? You know, there's another winter coming and . . . and you know, Annie, I'm not getting any younger, I can already feel the cold. I need a good jacket to keep me warm," I would kid her.

"Soon, Ranger. Soon, I think . . . before you get that old." Then she would get a twinkle in her eye and laugh before dropping her head to give me a sly little look.

"Do you have any more moose hides for me?" she would ask.

The promises continued throughout the winter, through the spring and summer. Soon it was fall, and another moose season was upon us, and still the jacket was "coming soon, Ranger".

Then the Division opened an office in Muskeg to service the Grande Cache District, and my trips to Grande Cache became less frequent. I knew that Annie could always use moose hides and they would never be wasted, so I continued to collect them, and by the end of the second hunting season I had gathered and given her more than thirty moose hides. Although I never saw any jackets around her cabin, it was obvious that Annie was busy working, turning out genuine Indian moosehide jackets, because the number of jackets on the street continued to increase.

Much to my chagrin, it had become painfully obvious that Annie's first priority was to fill the orders for paying customers. I couldn't really disagree with her logic. It is always better to serve the paying customers first. But I really wanted one of those jackets, and the more of them I saw, the more I wanted one. However, I am a patient man, and patience, I have often been told, is a virtue. My time would come. I had every confidence that in the end, I would receive my just reward.

Finally the inevitable happened. I was transferred. Soon I would be leaving Hinton and there would be no more trips, infrequently or otherwise, to Grande Cache. I had to have that jacket, now. I made a flying trip to Grande Cache to impress upon Annie the urgency of the moment.

"Hello, Ranger," Annie welcomed me. "Come in and have some tea. Have you got any more moose hides for me?"

"Hi, Annie," I returned her greeting as I walked into the cabin. "Sorry, no moosehides this trip. I was wondering, how's my jacket coming along?"

"How come you didn't bring me some moose hides?" she asked, ignoring my question completely.

"Well, I didn't have any this time, Annie," I replied, "but I was wondering if you've had a chance to finish my jacket yet?"

"When can I get some more moose hides?" Annie was a master at avoiding the question.

"I guess you'll have to wait for the moose season this fall, Annie," I replied.

"That's okay. You bring me some more moose hides then?" she said, still not committing to the jacket.

"I'm afraid I won't be able to," I told her. "I've been transferred to Calgary, but I'll tell my replacement that you can use some hides. I'm sure that he'll rustle you up some, especially when he sees the jacket you're making me. How does that sound?"

There was no answer. Annie just stared at me. She sat there for a long time, looking at the source of her moose hides drying up.

"I'll be leaving for Calgary in about six weeks' time," I said, breaking the silence. "I was sort of wondering if, maybe, you might be able to push my jacket up just a wee bit, Annie. You know, I've never even told my wife that you were making me a jacket. I want to surprise her with it. And I would love to be able to take it to Calgary with me," I pleaded. "Not many folks in Calgary have seen jackets as beautiful as the ones you make."

"I couldn't make you a jacket," Annie said. She gave me a hopeless look with sad eyes that never blinked. "Those moose hides you gave me, Ranger. They were no good."

"IT'S A STINKING ELK HEAD!"

"That's close enough!" roared His Honour, the presiding magistrate.

Oh, it was for sure a hot, very hot fall day. Many a handkerchief had been reduced to little more than a sopping-wet rag from wiping sweating brows. Outside there was not even the hint of a breeze to rustle the autumn leaves of the aspen that had turned the surrounding hills a golden colour. There was, however, the ever-present odour from the mill; and on beautiful days such as we were now experiencing, the stink enveloped the valley. There was no escape. Those destined to work in that locale suffered, and nerves were stretched to the limit; tempers grew short and often flared.

One day a week the travelling magistrate arrived in

Hinton to hold court, and this was the day. The courtroom, a modern room, was located in the town hall — in the valley, just a stone's throw across the road from the pulp mill. Inside the Hinton courtroom there was no escape from either the heat or the belching stink of the mill. But the heat inside was by far greater than that outside. It was a day that no one should have been in that room, whether they had to or not.

"I said, that's close enough!" bellowed His Honour for the second time. "STOP!" he roared, as he jumped to his feet. The quiet, stuffy, smelly little courtroom had suddenly taken on a new life. I think one would be safe and justified in saying that it had taken on a new air as the unbearable stench, a new stench, filled the room. Many of those seated in the courtroom had leapt to their feet before His Honour had, and they bolted for the door. Outside was the smell of the pulp mill, a far better option than what was on the inside.

This whole episode had started about three weeks earlier. I was just preparing to leave the office to help the regional fisheries biologist rehabilitate Cache Lake and Graveyard Lake. It was one of the tasks expected of me as a district officer, and I had been looking forward to it. It was a chance for me to redeem myself, to improve on the somewhat tarnished reputation I had somehow acquired for being an uncooperative officer when it came to biological matters. In fact, one of the local forest officers had asked if he could come along and help. The offer was accepted, for not only could he help, but he would be a witness to my complete commitment to furthering inter-branch relationships. I was just walking out the door on my way to pick up my brother officer, and to make amends, when the phone rang.

"Is the elk season open along the Lower Wildhay River Road?" asked the caller.

"Not till next week," I replied.

"Well, you'll be interested to know that someone has just shot a big bull elk a short distance east of the old ranger station. He's probably still there gutting the thing out. If you hurry, you just might catch him," advised the caller, then hung up the receiver.

I made an arbitrary decision to abandon the lake rehabilitation program and put the relation-mending on hold. I picked up the forest officer and we roared out of Hinton, heading for the Lower Wildhay River Road. The call had been legitimate, and on a hot fall day I soon took possession of a large six-point bull elk.

In the late sixties, seizing any wildlife in the Hinton district always created a problem for me, and seizing an animal the size of any bull elk in warm weather was nothing short of a disaster. Mar's freezer had been designated as restricted property. After our fiasco in Strathmore, she absolutely refused to let me use her freezer for government business. Not that it would have mattered — Mar's freezer would never have held a large six-point elk. But there were no cold-storage or freezer facilities available to me in town, a problem that had plagued me since my arrival. I made a quick call to the Powers That Be for help.

"I need a place to keep a large bull elk," I informed him.

"What have you got?" he asked.

"A trophy bull elk, the whole thing," I replied. There was dead silence on the other end of the line. Finally he spoke.

"Okay, bring it into Edson. I'll make the necessary arrangements," he assured me.

The rehabilitation project would have to proceed without me for a couple more hours.

"I made arrangements with one of the local butcher shops," I was informed when I arrived in Edson. "We can take it over there as long as it's quartered. They've got lots of room."

"It's all quartered and skinned, except for the head," I replied. "The guy that shot it is some irate. He says he wants his trophy back, that we're stealing it from him just because it's a big head. He also said he wants to cape it out himself, because he wants to have the head mounted. I'd say he's gonna plead not guilty, so we'll have to maintain continuity of the exhibits and make sure that head is kept just like it is."

"Don't worry about that," he replied. "I'll take possession of the exhibits and bring them to Hinton for court." With that, I turned the exhibits over to the Powers That Be. He signed the exhibit report, officially taking possession of the four quarters and the head with antlers still attached.

"So, where do I dump them?" I asked, anxious to get back to the lake rehabilitation project and my personal image restoration.

"You don't dump them anywhere," replied the Powers That Be. "We'll take them over to the butcher shop and you'll put them in the freezer for me!"

"Yeah," I replied, "that's exactly what I meant. Where do you want me to unload and store your exhibits?"

The butcher, however, had his own ideas regarding storage.

"That head and those horns aren't going into my freezer like that," he stated emphatically. "You'll have to cut the horns off. We can wrap the head up and I'll throw the horns in a shed for you. I don't want that head and horns in my freezer."

"No! No, you can't do that," I protested. "I need them for court just like they are. All in one piece."

"Your exhibits had better be brought to Hinton in the same condition as they are now," I told the Powers That Be.

"How long do I have to keep them like that?" asked the butcher.

"Only for a month or so," I replied.

"A month!" he snorted. "I can't keep them that long."

"They'll have to be kept frozen until after the trial," I said. "Please, it shouldn't take more than a month or so. I'll get them out of here as soon as possible."

"You're gonna have to pay for all the extra space them horns are gonna take up," the butcher said.

"We'll pay," replied the Powers That Be.

"You bet you will, and I want them out of here the minute that trial is over," he growled unhappily.

"You got it," I replied. "As soon as the trial is over, they're gone."

With the elk finally taken care of, my brother forest officer and I raced back to Hinton and out to Cache and Graveyard lakes to assist in the rehabilitation project. There was no one around by the time we arrived at the designated site. Alas, my reputation as being uncooperative would not be dispelled on this day.

The days passed quickly, and the trial was ready to begin. I was standing out in front of the courthouse waiting impatiently for the Powers That Be to arrive. He should have been there when court started, at ten in the morning. It was now past noon; we would be up as soon as court reconvened. This was not a good sign.

Finally he arrived, and none too soon. His Honour was getting a little antsy, not to mention a little hot under the collar.

"Whew!" I whistled and looked at the forest officer. I could smell my exhibits before I could see them. The powerful stench of rotting flesh drowned out the ever-present smell of the mill as the Powers That Be pulled his vehicle to a stop at the side of the building.

Loaded into a small trailer behind his vehicle I could see the antlers of the trophy elk protruding above the side boards.

"Oh no!" I gagged, as I watched him get out of his car and race towards the building. "Please tell me that smell isn't my exhibit."

"It is," he confirmed. "Let's get inside, quick." He charged past me through the door. Once inside, he drew in a deep breath, gasping for air.

"What did you do to my evidence?" I asked.

"The owner of the locker plant didn't want the head

in his freezer," he panted. "After we left, he put the bloody thing in a shed out back. I suppose you can tell it got a little high. But don't worry, I got it here for the trial."

"Did you bring the meat?" I asked.

"No, just the head. I didn't want to put the meat in with that putrefied mess. Nobody'd ever be able to eat it."

So it was that the main evidence stayed out in the parking lot when the trial commenced. There was no chance of anyone stealing it or tampering with it.

"And what did you see when you attended the scene, Officer?" asked the prosecutor. I was on the witness stand giving evidence for the Crown.

"The accused," I answered, and pointed to the defendant.

"What was the defendant doing?"

"He was dressing an elk, a large six-point bull elk," I replied.

"And is that elk in the courtroom today?"

"No sir, it's not. It's out in the parking lot," I responded.

"Your Honour," the prosecutor addressed the magistrate, "I would ask that if the accused agrees that the exhibit in question is an elk, that it be entered as an exhibit without having to be brought into the courtroom."

"If you wish to enter an exhibit, then you should produce it before the court," His Honour replied. He never looked up, just took his handkerchief and wiped the perspiration from his brow. The courtroom had become unbearably hot as the sun beat down.

"If it please the court, I would suggest that we adjourn to the parking lot, then, just to view the exhibit. I understand that it has taken on a—should I say, a certain air, Your Honour," cautioned the prosecutor.

"If you wish to enter an exhibit, then I need not tell you again that it must be brought before me," replied His Honour. He was slightly peeved at having to repeat himself, and he glared down at the prosecutor.

"As you wish, Your Honour. Officer, could you please bring the exhibit into the courtroom," requested the prosecutor. His nostrils, like those of the magistrate, had not yet sampled the air surrounding the rotting elk.

"Are you sure?" I asked. "Do you really want it in here? In the courtroom? It's really a stinking elk head."

"I don't care what kind of a stinking head it is," replied His Honour, leaning forward to assert his authority. "If you want to enter that head as an exhibit, you will bring it into this courtroom. Is that clear?"

"Very clear, Your Honour," I replied.

"Thank you, Officer! Then you are excused. Now, would you bring the exhibit so that I may enter it into the evidence," he growled, then sat back and waited.

The forest officer reluctantly volunteered to help me, and together we approached the elk head that lay stewing in the trailer. The flies and wasps were having a field day as they swarmed all over the decaying head.

Pulling the head off the trailer only served to enhance the stench, which gathered strength and reached new heights, if that was possible. Without a word to each other, we each took the tip of one antler, and clutching it firmly, we ran into the building, dragging the stinking elk head. Along the corridor we left a trail of rotting blood and a putrid, slimy, brownish-yellow liquid that was crawling with maggots.

Inside the hot, stuffy building the stink was absolutely unbearable. My brother forest officer had a very pained expression on his face. I gagged. My stomach was retching something fierce. I knew that any minute I was going to throw up. However, one must obey the commands of the court. We quickened our pace and raced down the hallway towards the courtroom.

We burst through the side doors of the courtroom, running towards the bench. I looked up and saw the horrified look on His Honour's face. Instantly the inside of the courtroom took on a rotten smell that a person can only imagine and hope to never encounter.

"That's close enough!" roared His Honour. "I said, that's close enough! STOP!" he bellowed as he jumped to his feet. "Get that thing out of my courtroom. Close court!" he screeched as he bolted from the courtroom.

The inside of the courtroom was bedlam. Chairs were knocked over, and the sound of heavy boots pounding on the tile floor filled the room. I was holding my breath and trying to keep my stomach from turning inside out when I glanced around and realized that the poor forest officer and myself were the only two people left in the room. Without a word we looked at each other and burst into laughter, then turned and raced from the room, with the stinking elk head in tow.

WILD HORSES

Wild horses! A fascinating subject that legends are made of. The mere mention of the words brought to mind the image of a magnificent stallion standing majestically on a rocky outcropping, his long mane blowing in the wind, surveying his herd of mares and colts grazing peacefully on the alpine meadow below.

Since my arrival in Hinton I had seen many horses in the wild. I had seen them when I was on foot, on horseback, in my car, and from the air. I had seen them back in the hills, in the forest, and on the edge of muskegs. But in all my travels, I had never seen the stallion or the mares that I imagined in the mountain setting. I had always assumed that the horses I saw were tame and belonged to someone. It was not uncommon to see livestock running at large throughout the forest. It was, after all, a very cost-effective way to feed one's livestock.

"People around these parts tell me that this country is full of wild horses," I said, broaching the topic of wild horses with the cowboy who sat drinking coffee in the Fish and Wildlife Office.

"Oh, there's wild horses around, all right," he replied, as he tilted his head back and peered at me from where he constantly hid under the brim of a large cowboy hat that was pulled down to almost cover his eyes.

"From time to time I see horses when I'm in the bush, but I always thought they were tame horses," I replied.

"Oh, there's some folks who just leave their horses running around out there, all right. But then, there's a lot of wild mustangs out there too," the cowboy assured me. I noticed that his voice rose with just a tinge of excitement at the mention of wild horses. "They run together."

"Some folks tell me you are a catcher of wild horses. That right?" I asked.

"Might be," he replied, and shifted his head slightly. I got a feeling that a suspicious eye was measuring me from under the brim of his hat.

"So, tell me, just how many of these wild horses do you catch in a year?" I asked.

"Hard to say," he answered evasively.

"One? Ten? Twenty? A hundred? Two hundred?" I pressed him.

"Yeah . . . you might say that." He wasn't going to commit himself to any number.

"What're the chances of me tagging along sometime?" I was testing him, for I was more than a little curious to know how it was done. I had heard

125

stories that wild-horse hunters used snares, which often caught more than just wild horses. I figured the cowboy would refuse, thereby confirming the stories. On the other hand, if he did agree, he might ask me to join him for what I expected would be a nice leisurely ride in the hills, avoiding both snares and wild horses.

"Why?" he asked, taking a slow sip of coffee and, I think, staring a hole right through me.

"Oh, no real reason . . ." I started to say, then shifted gears. "Well, some folks have been telling me that you use snares, and I just wanted to see for myself how it was that you could snare a horse without injuring it." I paused and smiled at him, but he wasn't smiling back. "Nah, not really, I just want to get me out of the office for a day or so."

"Some folks is wrong," said the cowboy, carefully measuring every word. I sensed a hint of anger in his voice.

"I guess I'll never know, will I?" I replied.

"Can you sit a horse?" he replied with a question of his own.

"Me? Yeah, I can sit a saddle," I answered nonchalantly.

"Sittin' a saddle is one thing, catchin' mustangs is another," he grunted. "It ain't no Sunday trail ride, you know." Once more I could feel the eyes I couldn't see. "Just how well do you sit the saddle?" he asked.

"Oh, I can sit a saddle pretty well, even if I do say so myself," I boasted. "I had a good ten months' practice when I was with the Horse Cops. Half a day, every day, clinging to a postage-stamp piece of leather they called an English saddle. Is that good enough, or do I have to ride better than that?"

"Ten months of trainin', huh?" He snickered. "Okay . . . sure, I think we can arrange somethin'. I can't wait to see just how good they train you boys," he chuckled, flashing a skeptical grin.

It was a clear, cold winter day when the cowboy decided that I could accompany him. He had two horses already saddled and loaded in the back of his stock truck when I met him before daybreak. We trucked south of Hinton, back into the foothills, before he pulled off onto a side road. This was the starting point of our hunt for wild horses.

"Are you looking for any wild horses in particular?" I asked a question just to make some conversation.

"I was told by a fella that he has a pinto stallion runnin' with a bunch down here. Says he'll pay a hundred dollars to the man that catches him and brings him back," he said. "I could use that hundred."

"Say you catch a pinto stallion, how will you know it's his? If there's no brand on it, it could be anybody's, or wild for that matter, couldn't it?"

"For a hundred bucks, it's his," replied the cowboy. "Now, I don't want no talkin' once we leave the truck. You open your mouth just once and I'll leave you here for wolf bait."

I questioned the order. "Why's that?"

"Because you're always yappin' and askin' questions like a teenage girl, that's why. We'll never see any horses with you yappin' all the time. At the sound of a whisper them wild horses will move back into the timber like a shadow and we'll never see 'em," he replied. "If we're going to catch us any horses, we gotta be able to see 'em. That means you keep your mouth shut. If you have to cough, you better swallow it."

"So, I keep my yap shut and we find some wild horses. Then what do we do?"

"Then you just hang on, boy, 'cause we're going to chase 'em down," he replied nonchalantly, making it sound like a walk in the park.

"You're just going to chase them down?" I repeated. I wasn't sure that I had heard him correctly.

"No, we're going to chase them down," he said again and stared at me for a minute from beneath the hat, giving me the same skeptical smile I had seen in the office. "You said you could ride, didn't you?"

"Yeah, I said I could ride, but I understood that you guys caught wild horses using snares?" This chasing bit put an entirely different slant on things.

"I told you, I don't use no snares," he scoffed unhappily. "You wouldn't be gettin' cold feet on me?"

"No. I'm fine," I mumbled, a little less sure of myself now that I had a better understanding of what the drill could be.

"That's good, 'cause you got old Midnight and he just loves to chase wild horses. Let's ride, then. You sure you're not just a little bit scared?" He chuckled.

"Nope, not yet anyway," I whispered as confidently as I could for his benefit, and also to ensure that I didn't scare any wild horses. "I just figure them mustangs ought to be able to run pretty fast."

"They can," he said, and smiled, "but we can run a

whole bunch faster and a whole bunch longer. That's if you can keep up."

"Don't get in my way," I crowed and swung up into the saddle. The cowboy gave me a skeptical look from under the hat. Then he turned and urged his horse forward.

We left the side road, the cowboy picking his way through the heavy spruce stand. He worked his way to the bottomland and carefully scanned a small muskeg bottom before he walked his horse into the open. Midnight played follow-the-leader, but he was not far behind; Midnight was raring to go. It was an easy ride as the horses slowly picked their way along old game trails. There was not a sound, except the creaking of the saddles and when a hoof occasionally struck a piece of deadfall.

At noon we stopped and ate our lunch in the saddle, and in silence. For some time now, I had had this feeling that the stories about snares might just be accurate. Not one wild horse had we seen, not even a horse track. In fact, we had not seen another animal. But it certainly was a nice day for a peaceful, quiet horse ride in the foothills, in the shadow of the Rockies. I was convinced that the cowboy had no intention of finding any wild horses, in snares or otherwise. The clever old fox was still hiding under his big hat as he poured a second cup of coffee. I smiled at him. A wild horse can't hear a smile, I thought.

Midnight had his nose right on the tail of the cowboy's horse as we walked out through a patch of willows onto a muskeg near mid-afternoon. Suddenly the cowboy let out a blood-curdling whoop. I could feel every muscle in Midnight's body tense as he jumped. I, too, jumped and just about fell out of the saddle.

"There they are!" yelled the cowboy and his voice rang out loud and clear, shattering the tranquillity of this peaceful day. In that instant I was jolted back to the world of the living, the reality of the day, catching wild horses.

The cowboy's horse sprang into action. I watched the animal go from a plowhorse walk to a racehorse gallop in a split second.

I knew immediately that Midnight was no stranger to wild-horse chases. He didn't wait for me to coax him to follow. The tensing muscles I had felt were actually coiled steel springs. Midnight's hind legs recoiled and he made a sudden jump straight up and forward. Midnight was not going to be left behind. He charged after the rapidly departing cowboy and his horse.

Being the skilled, trained rider that I was, I had almost regained the saddle after my first jolt. I had been deposited on Midnight's rump, behind the saddle, and I was hanging on for dear life as Midnight charged out onto the frozen muskeg. Lucky for me, I had a good grip on a short rein. I was able to snap the horse's head up and back, and slow his forward momentum, but only for a moment. The excited horse wanted desperately to be a part of the chase. He fought to gain a free head. I, on the other hand, wanted nothing more than to regain my seat. I was grabbing for the saddle horn, for his mane, for anything that would help me scramble back into the saddle.

By the time I got reseated and let Midnight have his head, the cowboy was about a hundred yards ahead of me. To him, this wild maniacal chase was the greatest thrill in the world.

"YEEEAAAHOOOOO! YEEEHHHAAAWWW! There's the pinto!" he howled at the top of his lungs as his horse charged across the muskeg.

Covered in a blanket of snow, the muskeg could have been a field. It was smooth and level. It was the ideal place to start the chase. On the far side, I spotted six horses racing in single file along the edge of the muskeg. In the lead was a beautiful pinto. The cowboy was right, I thought, he is a magnificent stallion. The pinto turned and the rapidly departing animals melted into a heavy stand of willows and spruce.

My peaceful horse ride in the foothills was over, forgotten as I found myself caught up in the excitement of the moment. Midnight was moving effortlessly under me, but trying desperately to get his nose back on the tail of the horse ahead of him. As he raced across the muskeg, I leaned forward over the saddle horn, feeling the cool, fresh winter air washing over my face. The back of the cowboy and the rump of his horse were my guiding beacons as they both glided effortlessly over the snow.

We were travelling at breakneck speed as we neared the centre of the muskeg. Poor old Midnight, he was not enjoying carrying the greenhorn and running more than a hundred yards behind the lead horse. Midnight was trying desperately to get his nose back on the leader's tail when suddenly, without warning, the scene in front of me changed. Although it happened in a split second, for me it was like watching a slow-motion picture from the best seat in the house, the saddle on Midnight.

The hind legs of the cowboy's horse drew up under his belly, but they never came down to power his next stride. They just kept going up, up, and up as the horse began to somersault. I watched in horror as the animal's entire belly, with his hind legs tucked tightly to it, came into view. The front legs were stretched out in front, burying themselves deeper into the snow. It must have been instinct because suddenly the horse kicked his hind legs straight back. Out they came, reaching for solid ground where there was only thin air. For an instant, the stretched-out animal seemed to be floating, slowly turning in the air as the somersault continued.

In that second, the cowboy was airborne, vaulting from the saddle as if he had been spring-loaded. Up into the air he sailed, in an arc that would have been graceful had it not been for the frantic flailing of arms and kicking of legs. In an uncontrolled nose dive, the cowboy sailed up and over the head of his horse. Then he was lost, out of sight, blotted out by the rising rump of his mount.

There was a loud, sharp crack, and the last I saw of the cowboy and his horse was the horse's belly and four legs pointing skyward, as both horse and rider disappeared and the scene in front of me returned to normal speed. Midnight and I were suddenly faced with an explosion of snow that erupted right in front of us.

Instinctively I reversed my position in the saddle,

moving so fast that I just about gave myself whiplash. I jammed both feet forward in the stirrups. I was standing in the stirrups, leaning back as far as I could and pulling on the reins with all my might, trying desperately to slam on the brakes.

"WHOA UP, MIDNIGHT!" I shouted. "WHOA, YOU STUPID JUGHEAD!"

But old Midnight was all pumped for the chase. He had been bred and trained to chase wild horses and he was following his instincts. He was fully prepared to charge into the chaos that was hidden but still unfolding in the cloud of snow billowing up in front of us. Midnight knew that somewhere on the other side of the melee there were wild horses running. He was fearless, wanting to continue the chase. He twisted, turned, and bucked as he fought the bit cutting into his mouth. The reluctant horse slowed, then stopped, but he continued to paw the snow as he pulled up just short of the scene of the crash.

In the settling snowflakes, I could see the cowboy's horse struggling to his feet on the far side of a huge depression in the snow, but the cowboy was nowhere in sight. He had fallen into a small creekbed. It was almost completely drifted over. Here and there, however, were little telltale shadows marking the banks where it snaked through the muskeg. The creek was completely invisible to the hard-riding cowboy and his horse. Their eyes had been trained on the shadows where the wild horses had disappeared into the forest, not on the gentle blanket of snow.

The cowboy's horse had not yet gained his feet when suddenly the cowboy's head popped out of the mound of snow that his horse had pushed up on the other side of the little creek. He sat up and frantically looked around.

"Which way did they go?" he demanded to know before he had even got to his feet. He snapped his head one way, then the other, in a dazed search for the mustangs.

I sat on my horse in stunned silence, not really believing what I was seeing. What really caught my attention were the two large blue globes protruding from an otherwise snow-covered face. The cowboy had lost his hat.

"Hey, you've got blue eyes!" I blurted out to the cowboy. "You look like a blue-eyed snowman!" I had often felt the glare of his eyes, but this was the first time it registered that the cowboy had eyes. And they were blue, bluer than the winter sky overhead.

"Which way did they go?" he screamed at me as he grabbed his hat and jammed it on his head before bouncing to his feet. He grabbed the reins of his mount, and with a mighty tug, pulled his horse to its feet. In one fluid motion he regained his saddle.

They both should be dead, I thought to myself, but only the cowboy's sense of direction seemed to have gotten just a mite fouled up during the spill. Sitting in the saddle, he had his horse spinning like a top as he frantically searched for the right direction to continue his chase.

"They went that-a-way," I finally told him, and

pointed towards the trees where I had last seen the disappearing rumps.

In a flash the cowboy, his blue eyes, his cowboy hat, and his horse were once again racing across the muskeg. The hidden creek had been only a temporary setback, one of the hazards of the trade, nothing more.

Midnight was also anxious to join this mad dash for the trees; however, I was a little more cautious. Scared would be a far better term. With my help Midnight picked his way across the hidden creek. The eager horse chomped at the bit and pranced the rest of the way across the muskeg. The cowboy was long gone before Midnight and I crossed the opening. He had not slowed down one little bit as he charged into the forest.

Even though the muskeg seemed to be free of further obstacles, I was taking no chances. I simply followed the cowboy's trail through the snow. Somewhere ahead the trail would end. I knew the cowboy had to be at the end of it; I would meet him there. I had not been trained for this kind of riding.

At the edge of the muskeg, with the cowboy, his horse, and the mustangs long gone, I figured it was safe to relax. This was not a wise decision. I had no sooner eased up when that darn fool of a horse bolted forward. His first burst of speed brought us under the branches and close to the trunk of a large spruce tree. Midnight was used to this bush-running; he ducked his head and went under the branches. I, on the other hand, was not so fortunate — I went through them.

"WHOA, MIDNIGHT! WHOA!" I screamed, as I realized too late that I faced more danger. But Midnight

135

was already too far behind the pack for his liking. He had either gone deaf or was no longer in a mood to obey my panicky scream. Midnight was a horse with a mission. He was after the pack, and unless I wanted to walk, I was along for the ride.

Through the spruce branches he carried me. I shut my eyes and threw my arms up to cover my face. When the branches and spruce needles stopped raking my flesh, I finally opened my eyes. There was more instant panic when I realized the speed with which Midnight was flying through the forest. He dodged in and out of trees with no regard for my safety or his own as he followed the well-marked trail. Midnight managed to miss each tree and dodge every snag, but I caught them all. I had the feeling that Midnight was getting even for being held back. He made sure that some part of my body bounced off or slammed into each obstacle as he galloped past.

Suddenly the nightmare of all nightmares loomed up in front of us. A deadfall, a fallen tree hung up on other trees, barred the trail. Would Midnight go over it or under it? It was an important decision and I had no idea what was on his mind. It was no time to leave my fate to Midnight. I heaved back on the reins in a futile attempt to stop the beast.

"WHOA, MIDNIGHT, WHOA!" I screamed the only words that seemed to be left in my vocabulary as once again I prepared to meet my Maker. Oblivious to my pleas, Midnight galloped on. At the last second I leaned over to one side in the saddle; again I shut my eyes, and I prayed.

"Please, Lord, don't let me die like this!" I wailed. My prayer was answered, for when I opened my eyes we had passed under the deadfall, and I was still in the saddle. Midnight never slowed down. He was bound and determined to catch the cowboy.

I sat up just in time to see Midnight pick an opening between two spruce trees. It was wide enough for a horse, but not a horse and rider.

"WHOA, MIDNIGHT, WHOA!" I bellered for the umpteenth time as Midnight charged between the two trees. Instantly, pain racked my legs as both knees slammed into the trees. I popped out of the saddle like a cork and sailed over the back end of Midnight. I never even touched his rump as he raced out from underneath me. But I hung on to the reins, clinging to them for dear life with both hands. My unexpected departure and two hundred pounds of dead weight on the reins snapped poor Midnight's head around and brought him to an abrupt halt. Midnight stood on one side of the trees, I sprawled on the other. He seemed to glare at me—he could not believe his bad luck, getting me for a rider.

I dragged myself between the trees and slowly crawled back onto the horse. This time I held a very tight rein. Midnight reluctantly followed the trail through the snow, but this time at my pace, a snail's pace. Far too slow for him, but far too fast for my aching body.

Midnight had walked for a long time, but not very far, when we abruptly came across a horse.

"It's a wild horse!" I exclaimed. The wild horse was

standing along the side of the trail. Suddenly my heart was racing.

"Hey, Midnight," I whispered to my trusty steed, "I'll betcha I can catch that horse. That'll sure surprise the cowboy." Then something inside spoke. "Don't even think about it, stupid. Haven't you had enough for one day?" The voice was right. I just looked at the wild horse. It stood there, its sides heaving from the exertion of the run, and watched as Midnight and I slowly walked past.

"Now, why wouldn't the cowboy take this horse?" I asked Midnight. That didn't make any sense to me. Here is a horse for the taking and the tracks showed clearly the cowboy had raced right by. The fool was probably going so fast he never even saw it. Or, you know, maybe he's still dazed from that fall. That has to be it, the fall.

A little farther along the trail, Midnight and I came upon a second horse. Another wild one, and just like the first, it was standing at the side of the trail. The third horse at the side of the trail was the stallion, the one-hundred-dollar pinto. It, too, just stood and watched us go by. I couldn't believe the cowboy had passed this one up as well. Before I finally found the cowboy, I had passed two more horses waiting for a soul far braver than me to pick them up. Not one of these horses had even tried to run as Midnight and I walked by; they just stood and watched us as we ambled along the trail.

We found the cowboy. He had finally come to his senses — he had stopped and picked up the sixth horse.

It was a snarky black horse, wild-eyed and mean-looking. But he was no match for the cowboy, who already had a rope and halter on him by the time old Midnight and I walked in. With extra rope he was building a makeshift corral for the animal.

"You missed five horses back there," I informed him. "They're just standing alongside the trail, in case you hadn't noticed."

"I noticed," he replied.

"How come you didn't take them when they stopped running?" I inquired.

"I can tell you don't know nothin' about wild horses," he grunted disgustedly. "Them's the poorest horses of the bunch, this one's the best. If I'da stopped for the first one, I woulda got only one. This way, I get 'em all. Anyway, I'm sorta surprised that you made it this far."

"Me too," I admitted.

"And you're still in the saddle!"

"Barely," I assured him, and I stayed in the saddle. I knew if I got off, I'd never get back on.

The cowboy was right. He raced back along the trail and I followed at a walk. Each time I caught up with him he was tying another horse into a makeshift rope corral. He had caught the entire herd. All six were tied into makeshift corrals.

"Only four wild ones," he complained. "Two of these nags got brands on 'em."

"Yeah, I couldn't believe you didn't stop and at least tie up that hundred-dollar pinto, the stallion," I chided him.

"You really don't know nothin' about horses, do you?" the cowboy snorted in disgust. "The stallions always run the longest, the fastest, the farthest. The stallion was the last horse, that mean little black one. The pinto's a mare."

"Right," I replied, nodding my head. "Right."

After a few minutes of silence, I dared myself to ask another undoubtedly stupid question as we rode away from the last horse: "Are you just going to leave those animals out here?"

"I'll come out with fresh horses and pick 'em up in the mornin'," he answered. "It'll give the stallion a little time to cool out and think about walkin' back with me. By the way, since you made it this far, I was figurin' that you might wanta come out in the morning and help me bring 'em in?"

"I'll have to see what's going on at the office first," I replied. "Give me a call tonight and I'll let you know."

Later that evening when the phone rang, I was sitting at home nursing the bruises on my body. Many were the size of dollar bills and they were far too numerous to count.

"How about it, pardner?" asked the cowboy in a cheery voice. "You ready to ride in the morning?"

"Sorry, looks like I've got a full day," I replied. "Nursing bruises," I added under my breath.

My secret life as a wild-horse chaser had come to an abrupt end. The office looked pretty good to me.

THE TRAPPER'S TEACUP

"Tell me, my friend, how does tea with a trapper sound to you?" I asked the young biologist.

"Really?" he replied, and his eyes lit up. I could tell that he was impressed. "You talked to the trappers and they asked you to stop in for tea?"

"Kind of . . ." I mumbled.

"Did you tell all the trappers that I was coming to see them, and that I'll be asking some questions?" asked the young biologist as he settled into the passenger seat of my '65 Chevy.

"Yeah, I did, sort of," I mumbled to my eager passenger.

"But you did talk to them? And you told them I wanted to talk to them about my survey?" he said excitedly.

"Oh, sure, I passed along the message to every trapper that I saw, just like you asked," I said, pulling away from the Hinton Fish and Wildlife Office.

My passenger and I were headed for the northern reaches of the Hinton Fish and Wildlife district. If need be, we would be going all the way to Grande Cache and beyond in our quest to find trappers. My task was to put him face to face with as many of the registered trappers in the area as possible.

"Are you trying to tell me you didn't contact every trapper in the area, like you were supposed to?" he asked. I noted a slight touch of annoyance in his voice.

"Now, how could I do that?" I asked. "Do you know how big this district is? But if it makes you feel any better, I do apologize because I didn't get to talk to them all." Well, I thought, one thing was certain, this trip was really not starting out on a good note.

"This isn't just a joyride, you know. I'm here to meet with trappers. I'm supposed to interview them, and I was told that you would set up the meetings."

"You know . . . well, let's just say it's really not as simple as all that," I replied. "Most of these trappers have a mind of their own. You may want to talk to them, but maybe they don't want to talk to you. Remember, these guys have just come in off their traplines after spending the whole winter out there in the bush. And some of them, if you'll pardon the expression, are a little bushed. You know, stir-crazy. They haven't had much contact with people. They don't trust anyone, especially someone they don't know. They can be a little spooky."

"I understand that," he said and gave me a look that didn't need any translation. This young biologist was no one's fool; he had been around.

"Good, " I said, "because when I talked to old Tom, he got a real funny look in his eyes. He wanted to know why you was comin' all the way out here to talk to him."

"And . . ." he said.

"And what?" I asked.

"And what did you tell him?"

"Nothing," I said. "I didn't tell him nothing. Nobody told me why you wanted to talk to trappers."

"How many of these trappers did you actually talk to?" he asked.

"Well . . . uh, I only talked to old Tom," I mumbled.

"Only one! You mean you only talked to one trapper? How will the rest know I want to talk to them, to question them, if you didn't let them know I was coming?" he asked. The young biologist sounded just a tad unhappy and a whole lot annoyed with me.

"The moccasin telegraph," I replied. "In this country it's very efficient. I suspect that by now every trapper in the country knows we're coming out to talk to them. And each one will probably have his own idea of what it's about."

"I don't think that's very professional," the biologist snorted in disgust.

"My guess is we'll just have to play it by ear," I replied. "If we're lucky enough to catch a trapper at his cabin, we just might be able to sit down and visit with him. If we're really lucky, one of them might even answer some of your questions."

"Tell me, exactly what did this Tom character say when you talked to him?"

"Well. Let me think now. As I recall, I was over at the post office and I bumped into old Tom on the sidewalk, just as I was walking out the door. We chatted for a couple of minutes — you know, sort of passing the time of day. Then I said, 'I'm gonna be out your way in a few days, Tom, and I thought I'd stop in and say hello.'

"'Anytime, Bobby,' he replied. 'Stop in anytime and have a cuppa tea with me.'"

"Well, that's good," replied the biologist. "That's the first encouraging thing I've heard yet."

"Yeah, well, then I said, 'Tom, I've got this biologist who's doing a survey. He's a pretty good guy. You'll like him, he'll be coming with me.'"

"And what did he say?" the young biologist asked, eager to hear what old Tom had to say.

"Well, you know, he never said a word. He stood there for a few seconds, eyeing me suspiciously. Then he turned and hightailed it out of there like a scalded cat," I said, describing old Tom's retreat. "Now, I did see him a couple of days later. He was ambling down the street like he didn't have a care in the world. Then he spotted me. In a flash, he had ducked between two buildings and had completely disappeared by the time I got there."

"Really?"

144

"Yeah, really," I replied. "I've seen him a couple of times, but he's avoiding me like the plague."

"And that's it? That's all you got for me?" he asked. "Well, you certainly don't appear to have a very good relationship with people in your district."

"That's it," I replied. "I know it's not much."

"That's okay, I guess," replied my passenger. For some reason he seemed to be feeling much better. "If that's the best you could do, that's it. I suppose I shouldn't have expected more. Well, let's go and find Tom and have that cup of tea. I like tea."

"Have you ever had tea with a trapper?" I asked. I looked at him and smiled.

"No," replied a rather surprised biologist. "Why? What harm is there in having a cup of tea?"

"None," I replied. "There isn't any harm in having a cup of tea, as long as you have a cup of tea. Just remember one thing — if you accept his invitation, whether you like it or not, you are going to be drinking that tea."

"Don't worry," he laughed. "What harm can there be in a cup of tea? I'll drink it. I like tea."

"Oh, you'll drink it all right. You can count on it," I smiled, "because you won't be leaving there until you do. Remember, my friend — to be forewarned is to be forearmed."

Our journey to Tom's cabin took us past Entrance. We took a side trip to Brûlé, then travelled past the Black Cat Ranch on our way to Rock Lake, Moberly, and the Big Berland. I stopped at every trapper's cabin on the way, but with no luck. There was not a sign, not even a hint of life at any of them.

Finally, up near the Big Berland, it appeared that our luck was about to change. We pulled up in front of a small log cabin that was built low to the ground, old Tom's cabin, and to my surprise there were signs of life. A thin column of smoke rose from the chimney and drifted into the pines. The door stood half-open. Inviting. It was a welcome sight for visitors.

"Well," I said, and couldn't hide the surprise in my voice, "it looks like you just might be in luck."

"This is it? This little thing is Tom's cabin?" asked the biologist. He looked a little bewildered.

"It certainly is," I said smugly, barely able to contain my own surprise. "This is old Tom's humble abode. You know, he was avoiding me in town, but it looks like he just might be brewing you that cup of tea, if you're still of a mind to accept his invitation."

"You should have told more trappers that we were coming," said the biologist, somewhat irritated. "Just think how many trappers I could have interviewed by now."

"It looks that way all right, doesn't it?" I replied, and shrugged my shoulders. How could one argue with such logic?

"You realize we've wasted the whole morning because you didn't do your job," he chided me.

"Hello, Tom," I called out, ignoring the comment, as we stepped from the car. But the only answer we received was the silence of the back country. In the distance a squirrel was kicking up quite a fuss, scolding an unknown intruder. We walked over to the open door. I stood to one side, and I knocked and quickly stepped back. We waited. There was nothing, not a sound. Then I leaned in and knocked again.

"Hello!" bellowed the biologist in my ear. The sudden, unexpected voice scared the tar right out of me. I just about climbed the wall.

"Let me know if you're gonna pull a stunt like that again," I snarled at him. My heart was pounding in my throat like crazy.

Very slowly, I looked inside. There were pelts everywhere. Squirrel and weasel were stacked on the table. The bed was covered with marten, mink, and a couple of fisher. Coyote, wolf, fox, and wolverine hung from the rafters. The pelts on the table had been pushed to one side, making room for a lone tin plate, a tin cup, and a large spoon. A pan was sitting on the stove, the beans in it sizzling and popping. I stepped inside, took the pan off the stove and set it on a block of wood, then quickly exited.

"It's empty. It looks like we must have interrupted his lunch," I mused. "He must have taken off out of here like a scared rabbit."

"I wonder where he's at," said my friend. He had a quizzical look on his face. "You did say he knew you were coming, didn't you?"

"Oh yeah," I replied. "He knew I was coming all right, and that you would be with me. My guess is that he heard us coming. That had to be his cue to get out, fast."

"Do you think he'll be right back?"

"Oh, I think so. I think he'll be right back as soon as we leave," I said, and laughed. "Well, so much for your tea with the trapper. This must be your lucky day."

"I don't know about you, but I could sure use a cup of tea and something to eat about now," replied the biologist.

"That sounds good to me," I replied. "I suppose that we could sit here for a few minutes and have our lunch," I replied.

"Are we gonna wait him out?" asked the biologist.

"Sure, if you want to. We can wait as long as you like," I replied. "After all, this is your trip."

I returned to the car and grabbed my Thermos and lunch, then sat down on a stump outside the cabin and poured a cup of coffee. My passenger the biologist stood there and looked at me with a long face.

"I thought we were going to have a cup of tea," he said.

"I've only got coffee," I replied. "Go get your Thermos."

"I mean, I thought we were going to have tea with the trapper. I don't drink coffee," he replied. "Can't we just make some tea in the cabin? The fire's already going. We could just make some tea and wait for him."

"Oh, I don't think that would be too wise," I said. "I know I am not going back in that cabin until we get a proper invite, from the trapper himself."

"But I didn't bring a Thermos with me," he mumbled.

I felt like saying, the river's full of water, you just go ahead and help yourself. But I didn't. I gave him half of my sandwich, and he passed on the coffee. We sat and listened to the sounds of the forest. The chatter of the red squirrel. The call of the whisky-jack. The breeze whistling through the pines. There were lots of sounds in the forest, but not one of them included the sound of a trapper returning to his cabin. Obviously old Tom didn't want any more to do with me at his cabin than he did in town.

Accepting the fact that old Tom was not about to show himself, we climbed back in my vehicle. As I was backing up to turn around, I caught a glimpse of a tall, thin man in the rear-view mirror. Old Tom had stepped out of his hiding place a second too soon. Once more I stepped out of the vehicle, turned to face the tree where he disappeared, and called, "Hey, Tom, it's me, Bob! I brought the biologist out that I was telling you about. He'd like to meet you." Then I waved to him and walked over to the tree.

Old Tom was standing there, stiff as a board, behind that tree; it was as if he was frozen in time. As I got closer, the only movement I could detect was coming from his eyes. His eyes were ablaze, darting around in his head like they belonged in a pinball machine. He looked to me like a cornered animal. Afraid! Caught! Should he stay? Should he run? The indiscretion and the moment of indecision had cost him.

"How are you today, my friend?" I asked, but ventured no closer for Tom's darting eyes had slowed down some — although they were still bouncing around in his head, I had this feeling that they were settling in on me. Tom hadn't decided whether or not I was his

149

friend, and he looked like he might bolt for the trees at any second.

"Hello, Tom," chirped up the biologist who suddenly appeared off to one side. He had left the car and was heading toward Tom with a clipboard in his hand. Suddenly, Tom's eyes went into another fit of spinning in his head, and the biologist stopped dead in his tracks.

"What's the matter with him?" the biologist whispered to me, his eyes never leaving Tom.

"I'm not sure," I replied. "He's probably sizing us up, deciding whether he should shoot us and skin us, or invite us in."

"Really?" asked the biologist. "Do you think he might shoot us?"

"I'm only kidding," I replied. "I don't have a clue what's going on in his head."

Tom stood behind his tree for the longest time. Finally his eyes settled down, and their only movement was repeatedly looking from me to the biologist and back. Then, without a word, he stepped out and walked back to his cabin. All was quiet in the cabin and we waited, standing at the edge of the forest like two statues, or as some might say, two dummies.

"What are we gonna do, stand here all day?" asked the biologist in a hushed tone.

"Could be," I replied, being just as quiet. "We'll just wait and see what he does. You know, I just remembered, there's a rumour going around that old Tom here had a shootout with another trapper a couple of years ago. When the shooting stopped, a couple days later, neither one could remember who started the shooting or why."

About that time, I heard a rustling sound and noticed that the biologist had slipped back into the car.

"I think we should leave," he said. "We're a long way from anywhere and nobody knows where we are. I don't like this, and I don't think it's safe."

I was just about to say he was right on all counts, when Tom suddenly appeared in the doorway. Tom's eyes had really settled down in his head and he watched us cautiously, skeptically. I stayed frozen where I was and breathed a sigh of relief when Tom turned and disappeared back into the cabin.

"You comin' in, or you jist gonna stand outside?" came a high-pitched voice that scared the dickens right out of me. Tom had made up his mind, we could come in.

"We're coming in, Tom," I called back, then turned to the biologist and in a low voice said, "Remember, whatever you do, don't accept a cup of tea from him. Tell him we've already eaten. But if you do—remember, you're gonna have to drink it."

"Gotcha," he replied and his eyes were riveted on the cabin door. "But are you sure it's safe to go in there?"

"I have no idea, but we're about to find out. I suppose if we don't come out, we'll know it wasn't," I said, trying to make light of it, for I wasn't any happier about this encounter with Tom than he was right now.

"Sit yerself down," Tom said, and pointed to a couple of blocks of firewood that had been stood on end. They would serve as the chairs. With the sweep of one big paw Tom cleared the table. It was now as clean as it was going to get. His pelts were strewn about the floor.

"Move yer stumps over to the table and we'll have a cup of tea," Tom said.

"No tea for me, Tom," I replied. I looked above the table. Several pelts dangled down. They were being inspected by some huge, black beetles. "I just had a big lunch and some coffee."

Tom stopped and gave me a look that said he didn't believe me.

"Honest, Tom. I'm full. I didn't know you were home, so I ate," I added quickly. "We had us a nice little picnic, right here beside your cabin."

"What about you? Did you have a picnic too?" Tom sort of snarled at the biologist.

"Naw, he don't want any —" I started to say, but was cut short.

"Please, I'd like some tea," said the biologist much to my surprise as he reached down with both hands and pulled his stump of a log closer to the table.

"And he's gonna drink every last drop of it too," I promised Tom. "He tells me he really likes tea." I looked at my partner and shook my head.

"So, Tom, how was trapping this year?" I asked, craning my neck to peer around a wolf pelt that was dangling between us. Tom ignored the question and busied himself making the tea. Both the biologist and I asked Tom a number of questions about the trapping season. But Tom wasn't answering, he was busy making the tea.

I could not suppress the smile that tickled my lips as Tom got ready to serve his guest. I watched the biologist and saw his mouth drop when Tom picked up an old coffee mug. It was the type of mug they used in all the railroad beaneries along the CNR line, but for now it was the trapper's teacup. Tom pulled the tail of his dirty old shirt out of his filthy trousers, the ones he had put on last fall and probably hadn't taken off yet, and wiped off the outside of that mug. He held it up to inspect it, obviously it passed the inspection, then he plunked that mug on the table, right in front of his special guest.

The poor biologist, he sat there and stared at that heavy old coffee mug. Finally he looked up at Tom, then at me, then back at the cup. There was a sickly smile on his face. He could not believe what he was seeing or the fate the gods had dealt him.

The outside of that old coffee cup was smeared as clean as Tom could smear it with his dirty old shirt. But the inside, now, that was another matter. A thick layer of black grunge coated—no, coated is the wrong word—it was plastered to the inside of the cup. A small, neat, round hole, close to the centre of the mug and the grunge, appeared to go right down to the bottom of the cup. It looked suspiciously as if Tom had taken his finger and drilled that hole in there, making enough room for at least a spot of tea.

"Don't forget," I said to the biologist, for I just could not help myself, "every last drop."

Tom picked an old coffee pot off the stove, where the tea had been boiling for several minutes. Into that black hole he poured the blackest, thickest liquid imaginable. Tom should have filled the mug before he brought it to the table, because now that the tea was poured, it was impossible to tell where the grunge ended and the tea began, or vice versa. The tea, the grunge, and the trapper's teacup became one, a black gob on an equally filthy table.

"Are you sure you won't join your friend here for a cup of tea?" Tom asked me.

"Thanks anyway, Tom," I replied quickly, "but I'm full up. I don't think I could chew another drop."

"I-I don't think???????I don't think I'm very thirsty either," mumbled the biologist in a sickly voice.

I could see the fire returning to Tom's eyes as they darted back and forth between the teacup and the biologist.

"He's just kidding, Tom," I quickly assured the trapper. "He's not used to tea with this much body." Then I turned and addressed the young biologist. "Now, I know you're thirsty and I know you love tea. Drink! And remember, every last drop."

The biologist sat there looking at his tea. He was getting greener by the minute. The trapper stood there looking at the biologist, getting more agitated by the minute. Suddenly, from out of nowhere, a missile landed with a plop right smack dab in the middle of the teacup. Half a dozen drops of tea arced out and splatted on the dirty tabletop.

We all leaned forward and looked at a huge black

beetle that must have lost his grip on the fox pelt and plunged, or dove, into the tea. The beetle disappeared as he plunged to the bottom of the cup. Then, like a cork, the beetle popped to the top, did a couple of breast strokes and reached the grunge at the side of the cup. He tested the footing several times and, finally finding it to his liking, he climbed out. He paused on the grunge long enough to shake off a couple of drops of tea, then fell over the lip of the cup onto the table. The biologist's eyes bulged like giant marbles as he stared into the cup.

"I think your tea is cool enough to drink now," I said, and I smiled at the biologist.

HE NEVER SAID GOODBYE

It was in mid-June when I met the two on the street. We had passed many times before, and each time I would acknowledge them. But they never replied, they never said hello. This time, I was surprised when the smaller man spoke. We have come a long way, I thought, and I smiled as memories came racing back.

*   *   *

The incident report read: Two moose shot and left on the road between Brûlé and Rock Lake. The carcasses are hidden, buried under a mound of snow, on the north side of the road. They are in a stand of spruce about two miles south of the bridge on the Wildhay River. The identity of the hunters is unknown.

"It was probably them there Longhairs," said the trapper who had stopped in at the Fish and Wildlife Office to report the find. He mentioned Longhairs as if this sort of event were an ordinary occurrence.

"Who?" I asked. I had not heard the term "Longhairs" before, and I certainly had no idea who the Longhairs might be.

"The Longhairs," he repeated. "You know them, don'tcha? They're a bunch of Indians who moved up here from the south. They're all treaty Indians, you know."

"No, I didn't know," I responded.

"Yeah, they're Treaties all right, and Treaties can hunt anytime."

"Now, that I know," I assured him.

"Oh, yeah. They're Treaties all right, and they can hunt anytime they want to," he stated. "I wouldn't even waste my time going out there if I was you."

"Is that right?" I replied, looking him in the eye. "Tell me, if you know these moose were shot by Treaties, then why are you telling me?"

"I don't rightly know," he replied, and looked at me with a twinkle in his eyes. "Something about that kill site, I guess," he said, shaking his head. "But the more I think about it, I think it's got to be the Longhairs, nobody else would go hunting when it's this cold. A man would have to be tetched in the head, crazy to go out in this weather unless he really had to." Then he gave me a funny look and added, "You ain't planning on going out there, are you?"

"I reckon so," I replied. "Since you've lodged a complaint, I'm obliged to at least go and have a look at it. But you're probably right, it will turn out to be an Indian kill."

"I know you ain't askin', but if you was to ask, I'd

157

say forget it. Stay home where it's warm." Then he walked over to the front window and looked out. "Look, it's a clear sky. It's gonna get real cold, might even go to fifty below tonight in the mountains. A man could freeze to death out there and nobody'd find him till spring."

It was the last week in January, and the moose season had been closed for a couple of months. The temperature had been hovering around thirty below zero. The old trapper was right—with a clear sky it could hit forty below tonight.

After leaving Hinton, I crossed the bridge over the Athabasca River. There the road, which some said was the old Grand Trunk railroad bed, followed the north bank of the river. I drove past the ranger station at Entrance, heading towards Brûlé. The road was a narrow washboard that just about shook my insides out, and I was relieved when I turned onto the old forestry road after I crossed the small bridge on Solomon Creek. The road snaked northward, following the banks of Solomon Creek. I passed the Black Cat Ranch. It was deserted; there was no sign of any activity around the empty buildings. The brown, dried grass of winter protruding through the snow had grown taller than the windowsills. As I wound my way through the forest, I noticed there hadn't been very much traffic on the road either.

A couple of miles before reaching the Wildhay I found tracks where a vehicle had pulled over to the side of the road. There were more than one set of footprints in the snow leading into the bush. I followed the tracks for about fifty yards, and I found two mounds of snow that I presumed covered two moose carcasses. The moose carcasses, if that's what they were, were completely covered with snow, and if a person hadn't known that they were supposed to be there, they could have been easily bypassed.

I checked the area for any evidence that might have been left behind—cigarette packages, papers, knives, anything at all—but came up empty-handed. Since there was no evidence lying around, I checked to see if any animal parts had been hung in trees. I was hoping for the telltale sign that the kills had been made by Natives, so I could go home. It was customary for many of the Indians to hang a part of the animal in a tree as an offering and for good luck.

"Please, Lord," I prayed, "let me find a bell or some part draped across a limb." Often it was the moose's bell, the long, hairy fold of skin that hangs below the neck. This was not to be my lucky day, I thought, as I searched the trees. There was not a single hair to be found on any limb.

Since it was not an obvious Native kill, I decided to check the animals. Maybe, with just a little bit of luck, there'll be a couple of wild horses under those mounds, I thought, and an evil grin gripped my freezing face. Now that would be nice, because then I could turn the file over to the RCMP and I could go home where it was nice and warm. I bent over the smaller mound, and extending a gloved hand, attempted to brush some of the snow off the smallest animal. It was like trying to brush frost off a windshield, and I succeeded in stirring only a wisp of snow that was covering what appeared to be just a mound of ice.

I stood up and surveyed the surrounding terrain before turning my attention back to the frozen mounds. They weren't natural; they were man-made. Someone had deliberately built them.

Again I bent over the mound and examined it. Then I rapped on the surface. It was like knocking on a door, an ice door. Tap tapa-tapa-tap tap, the sound echoed in the crisp stillness. The mound sounded hollow, so I raised my fist and I gave it a good bang.

My fist slammed through a good half-inch layer of ice. The force of the blow took my fist and my arm and almost the rest of me into the hole. I struggled to maintain my balance and was greeted by a gush of putrid, sour steam that blasted through the opening. The stench of sour meat erupted into my face. It was hot, it was moist, and it was enough to gag a maggot.

"Oh, my ever-lovin' oath!" I gasped, then retched as the gag reflex gripped my throat. I staggered backward, fighting the overwhelming urge to vomit. The escaping steam instantly froze on everything it came in contact with, or turned into ice crystals in the frigid air. The fur trim on my parka, my eyelashes, my eyebrows, and I'm sure the hair in my nose, all immediately glistened with frost. Putrid, gagging, foul-smelling frost. I tried desperately to brush myself clean, but only succeeded in grinding the smell deeper into my face and clothes.

"What in the name of . . . have I got here?" I moaned as I fell back against a tree, gasping for fresh air. When my stomach had settled, I cleared enough snow and ice away from the steaming hole to get a good look inside the mound and confirm the presence of a moose calf — one stinking, rotting moose calf. The spruce branches above the calf were taking on a thick layer of frost as steam continued to belch from the opening. I knew the bigger mound contained another moose, probably a cow. It could stay undisturbed and stink just the way it was for the time being.

The way I figured it, the animals must have been covered immediately after they were shot. The heat from their bodies melted the snow, and in the very cold weather, a layer of ice had formed around the carcasses and sealed in the heat. Both carcasses had turned sour, and to my way of thinking, they had to be beyond salvage.

The old trapper had been right — there were two moose and it was colder than all get-out. A guy would have to be a little tetched in the head to come out in this weather, let alone stick around. At this point I was having a terrible argument with myself. I knew that if someone had gone to the trouble of covering the animals, he would return for them. If I wanted to meet this hunter, I was going to have to wait and see.

"Now, let's see," I muttered out loud, "just how tetched in the head am I?"

"You're tetched, all right," I said to myself as I moved my vehicle down towards the river away from the kill site. "You should take the old trapper's advice, forget about this nonsense and go home where it's nice and warm." But being tetched, logic was not an option and stupidity reigned supreme.

Reluctantly, I dragged my not-yet-thawed butt out of the car and trudged back up the road to the scene of the crime. There I picked out a nice hiding spot, behind a large spruce tree and a clump of alders, where I could keep an eye on the road and the carcasses. It was the beginning of a lesson of a lifetime, for it was here, in the middle of nowhere, in the middle of winter, in the middle of the coldest spell of the year, that I learned the true meaning of the word "cold".

Sitting and waiting, watching a crime scene, had always been to me more boring than watching paint dry, but sitting and watching a crime scene in forty-below weather was totally absurd.

"When this is over, I should really consider going and having my tetched head read," I mumbled, as once more the cold worked its way through my clothing. I hadn't stopped shivering since I first got out of the car.

I had lots of time to think while the frost played havoc, numbing my nose, my toes, and my fingers. What if I sit here all day, I thought, and can't get my vehicle started when I'm ready to leave? Worse yet, what if they show up and I have to ask them for a boost? Would that be more embarrassing than the time I had to ask a violator to borrow his pen so I could write him up a ticket? This little situation had the potential to be one of life's embarrassing moments, if not very serious consequences for Mrs. Adams' little boy, Bobby. If no one showed up and the car wouldn't start, I was in for a mighty long walk in this weather. There was no one at Rock Lake, there was no one at the Black Cat Dude Ranch, and there was probably not going to be anybody coming down this seldom-used road either. The more I thought about it, the more I was convinced that the old trapper might have been right, and I should have stayed home.

I tried squatting down and huddling into the snow.

The moose must have had a better heating system than I did, because I didn't generate any heat or steam. My feet and legs seemed to be getting colder instead of warmer. I stood up, stamped my feet, waved my arms, and patiently froze under the spruce. If I concentrated, and I had a lot of time to concentrate, I could actually watch the icicles forming on the strands of fur around the trim on my parka. Each breath would deposit another thin layer. I had little icicles hanging from the fine fur; they dangled sparkling crystals in front of my face.

Finally, I could take it no longer. I decided, illegal moose or not, if I didn't do something real soon, I was going to become a permanent part of the frozen landscape. This wasn't a normal stakeout, and illegal moose or not, I wasn't about to be the most diligent observer. I would try to avoid embarrassment and hopefully save my life.

I left my post and shuffled back to my car. There, I broke the icicles and a fair amount of fur trim off my parka before getting in, and turned the key in the ignition. Grudgingly the motor kicked in, and the fan started to blow a freezing blast. It was winter air, straight from the Arctic.

As the inside of the car began to warm, the little icicles started to melt. The sour smell of the moose returned. The stench got worse as the car warmed. By the time I turned off the motor and returned to the spruce tree, I wasn't sure which I preferred, the cold or the stench.

Every hour or so I would repeat this little routine, and every time I left the vehicle the bitter cold would slice right through me. But I waited. As darkness enveloped me, the temperature plunged even farther. And still I waited. All that miserable day and through the long, bitterly cold night, the longest night of my life, I shivered and I shook and I cursed and I waited. During all that time, the forest and the mountains were deathly silent. There was not a sound from the wilds of western Alberta, not a squirrel, not a jay, not a breeze whispering through the spruce and pine. And most importantly, there was not the roar of a vehicle. The eerie silence was only broken by the sounds of arms flapping, hands clapping, and feet stomping. It was the futile attempts of a tetched-in-the-head Fish Cop struggling to keep the blood circulating, too bullheaded to admit defeat.

When dawn broke, I was still in the spruce trees, still two miles from the Wildhay River, still in the valley, still in the shadow of the Rockies. From where I huddled, I watched the progress of the sun as it rose in the east. I saw the first rays touch the peaks of the snow-covered mountains. I watched as the sun slowly crept down the rugged slopes, giving a soft pinkish hue to the rocks and snow as it kissed them. It would be another clear, sunny, miserably cold winter day.

By mid-morning I not only looked like an icicle, I felt like an icicle. My mind started to play games on me. I imagined that I could hear sounds. Strange yet familiar sounds. I held my breath and strained my ears in an attempt to hear something, anything. At one point I stopped suddenly — very distinctly I heard the tinkling of wind chimes. I listened again, not moving, but there was no sound. I was sure that I had heard wind chimes. Maybe, I thought, there were icicles hanging from the hairs on the inside of my nose. That had to be it. There could be nothing else on such a calm day.

Finally, I had had enough. I was ready to call it quits and reluctantly admit that I should have listened to the old trapper and stayed at home where it was warm and toasty. Now I'd be haunted by his words: "That young game warden, he's a little tetched in the head. Stayed out all night in forty-below weather."

Then in the distance, echoing through the forest, I heard it.

"There," I shouted happily, "I heard that! It's a motor! Someone's coming!" Indeed, it was the unmistakable sound of a motor. A vehicle was coming. I seemed to hear the drone in the crisp frosty air for an eternity, but it grew louder, and then a truck slowly crept into view. It approached the scene and then stopped opposite the tracks in the snow. I could see three people in the cab of a pickup. I was very still — or perhaps I was frozen stiff — I couldn't remember, but I knew I couldn't move. Even if I wanted to, movement would be very difficult, maybe impossible. I watched as the three sat there, taking their time in the comfort of their nice warm truck. What were they saying? What were they thinking? Why didn't they get out? Sure, I thought, here I am freezing my butt off and these mothers are sitting in a nice warm vehicle.

"Hurry up and get out!" I was yelling under my breath. "I want to get this over with and get home where it's warm."

After what seemed to be a lifetime—at least, a life frozen in time—a door opened, and they finally got out of the vehicle. Without hesitating, they walked into the bush. I held my breath for fear they would see it in the frigid air. But I was the least of their worries as they headed straight towards the two mounds of snow.

"Ha!" I muttered half out loud. "As soon as you kick into that first mound of snow you get two surprises. Instant barf and instant Bob right in your face." After babysitting these moose for the past twenty-four hours in the freezing cold, I was ready for action. I tried to smile, but my face wouldn't work.

The first person reached the animals, and just like I knew he would, he kicked at the mound. The icy mound cracked and popped as he drove his foot into it. A gaping hole appeared and instantly a cloud of steam belched forth, engulfing him. For a second he was hidden from view in the vapours that were rapidly turning to ice crystals. I had visions of him bent over, vomiting from deep within the pit of his stomach, but when he appeared through the cloud, he was showing no ill effect. He didn't recoil as I had anticipated. In fact, he just continued to kick more snow and ice off the moose. Well, if the smell didn't get his attention, I consoled myself, I knew what would send the fear of the Lord into him.

"Hold it right where you are!" I roared in my best frozen voice, noticing that my jaw hardly moved, it was so cold. "Don't anyone move! You're all covered!" I heard myself deliver the orders, and realized that my voice wasn't roaring the way I intended. There was no authority, no take-charge sound; there was only a feeble squeak. "Oh no," I moaned. "Even my voice box is frozen."

My surprise appearance and less-than-masculine voice had about as much impact on them as the sour moose smell had. They slowly turned and gazed in my direction. I moved out from behind the tree on feet that I could no longer feel and stumbled towards them.

"Oh, boy," I thought, "I'll bet I'm just throwing the fear of the Lord into them right now."

As I shuffled closer to them, my heart sank. For just like the cloud of steam that was billowing up from the open mound, I could see twenty-four hours of freezing half to death and my dream of a big bust drifting away. I stopped and stared at the braids. I was looking into the faces of three men who, although I had never met them before, I instinctively knew were the "Longhairs".

My heart wasn't in the questions I had to ask, because I had a sinking feeling I knew beforehand what the answers would be. Suddenly I felt colder; in fact, I felt colder and older, and a little tetched in the head.

"You fellows know who shot these animals?" I asked, mumbling through quivering lips.

"I did," came the reply from one of the three.

"Yeah, and just who might you be?" I inquired, and wished that I were home where it was nice and warm.

"We're Indians. We got treaty rights."

"Good. Have you got any identification?" I asked, peering through the icicles that hung from the parka trim. I stamped my feet, hoping to detect some feeling. "Man, my feet are cold," I mumbled.

At my request for ID, one of the men produced a driver's licence.

"This tells me you can drive," I told him. "Now, what authority do you have to hunt out of season?" Boy, my fingers are just about frozen, I thought, as I realized I was having trouble holding on to the licence.

"We're treaty Indians."

"Yeah, sure you are," I tried to chuckle, but it was too cold. "Can I see your treaty cards?" I was getting nowhere fast. "Aren't you guys cold?" I asked, noticing that I was the only one shivering like a poplar leaf in a windstorm.

"We don't carry treaty cards," he replied, ignoring my question about the cold.

I knew that, but how did I know that? With my half-frozen brain, I tried to remember where I had heard that before. Somewhere, I seemed to recall, someone had told me about a group of Indians in the area that had never signed a treaty. They also refused to sign anything regarding wildlife, but they were eligible for status and therefore enjoyed treaty hunting and fishing privileges. They believed that signing anything would cause them to lose their spirit. Was I looking at three individuals who were eligible for status and entitled to treaty rights? Was this the reason I had sat up all night and frozen? If so, there had to be something wrong with the picture.

"Okay," I said. "If my pen's not frozen, I'll take down your names and check you out. If you're not eligible for treaty rights, you'll all be charged for hunting out of season. Do you understand that?"

"That's okay," one of them replied. "Do you want to take this meat out for us, too? We don't mind." They all thought that was very funny.

"I doubt it, but I'm curious — are you going to use that meat?" I asked. "It's pretty sour. I about puked when I opened it yesterday."

"It's okay," he assured me.

"Remember, you can't allow meat to spoil," I cautioned them. "Treaty rights don't give you the right to allow edible meat to spoil."

"We'll eat it," he replied.

The snow crunched under my feet as I trudged back to my vehicle. "I must be a sorry sight," I mumbled to myself. My body shivered violently. "I think maybe I'll go and have a talk with one of the Elders. That is, if I ever thaw out." The heater fan was once again blowing Arctic air into the cab.

* * *

The Indian camp was a loose collection of tents about half a mile south of Highway 16, a couple of miles east of the Jasper Park gates. About a week had passed since I had spent the night with the moose. My body had finally returned to normal, with only the odd spasm of shivering whenever I walked outside. I slowed on Highway 16 and turned south towards their camp.

The tents were in a small clump of spruce trees tucked away in a grove of poplars and were easily seen now that there were no leaves on the trees. I noticed that smoke was coming from the chimney of every tent when I drove in, but there was no one in sight. Not a soul. I approached the nearest tent.

"Anyone home?" I called out, and waited. There was no response. I went to a couple of more tents and called out again. Still no reply.

"I'm here to talk to one of the Elders, or the Chief," I called out loudly, certain that this disclosure would get results. Still nothing.

I returned to my vehicle and slowly left the camp with its mysterious, non-existent occupants.

The morning after I had been to the tent camp, I was surprised when two men walked into my office. They must have been waiting for me, as I had barely opened the doors when they entered. One had long, braided hair. The other's hair was short. They walked through the door and stood looking straight ahead. Neither one spoke a word. They just stood there. They were the Longhairs.

"Good day, gentlemen!" I greeted them as I did all visitors. "What can I do for you today?"

Neither spoke a single word of acknowledgement. They just stared at me.

"Well, would you gentlemen like to come into my office?" I asked, inviting them to join me in the back office. Without a word, both walked right past me into the office, and sat down in the two chairs that faced my desk.

"Have a seat, gentlemen." I made the offer somewhat belatedly. "Would either of you like a cup of coffee?" I asked. Both sat. Still neither said a word. They both just sat there, watching me, waiting.

We sat across the desk from each other, only a few feet away, yet worlds apart.

One of my guests was a thin man with a very small, round face. He was not very tall. His dark eyes never left me and they showed no emotion whatsoever. The other was a much taller man, also very slim, with high cheekbones. They both sat and looked at me. Neither spoke.

It didn't take a rocket scientist to realize that if there was going to be any talking, it was going to have to come from me. My guests were there voluntarily, but it was clear they were there to listen, not to talk.

Okay, hotshot, I thought, you wanted this meeting, now take your best shot and let the chips fall where they may. I had not been introduced to either of the two, but I had a good idea who they were.

I broke the silence and introduced myself, then added, "And I take it you two gentlemen are from the camp out by Folding Mountain." Neither man showed any sign of recognition or acknowledgement.

"First of all, gentlemen —" I stopped. "Or would you prefer to be addressed in another fashion, by your names perhaps?" I asked, hoping to find out exactly who they were. I looked at both of them for some indication of their preference, and hopefully a name or two. But no such luck. The unblinking dark eyes remained fixed on me. There was no answer to be gained from them.

"If you prefer to be addressed in another way, please let me know," I said. "I want to thank you both for coming in today," I began slowly. "I have a problem and I need help—your help, if you agree. I understand that you are status Indians, and as such you are entitled to treaty rights. If that is true, then you can pursue your hunting and fishing rights at any time of the year on any land that you have a right of access to. I know the rights that were granted to you in this regard, and I respect those rights. I will do whatever I can to ensure that you continue to enjoy those rights."

I waited to see what effect this statement had. Obviously none, for there was still no comment, no movement, only the dark eyes that never left my face. I continued.

"This is my problem," I began hesitantly. "Last week three men who said they were members of your band shot two moose out by the Wildhay River near Rock Lake. Now, if they have status rights, then everything is legitimate. But you see, they did not have treaty cards with them, and I have no way of knowing if they are entitled to treaty privileges."

The man with the long hair moved in his chair. He reached into his pants pocket, and he pulled out a card and held it out for me to see. I reached out to take it and then realized that he wasn't about to let it go. He would hold it while I read it. I leaned forward and took a good look. It was a business card from one of the Powers That Be; it even bore his signature.

"Now I remember . . ." I said. In my frozen state at the kill site, I had had a faint recollection of this, but it didn't register then. "The Powers That Be told me that there was a group of Indians who sometimes came to this area, who were eligible for treaty status. So, that would be your group, right?"

Without a word, the card, having served its purpose, was returned to the pocket.

"There is one more thing that you gentlemen can help me with," I continued, since I was on a roll and we were now communicating. "I sat with those moose for a day, a night, and half the next day—more than twenty-four hours in minus-forty-degree weather. I just about froze to death. Now, I can't stop you or your people from hunting for food, nor would I want to. I just don't want to freeze my butt off anymore. I would much prefer to spend my time doing something useful rather than sitting in the bush all night. So I was wondering if maybe you would be able to help me?"

I sat there, expectantly, waiting for either one to say something. Anything at all. I looked first at one, then at the other. Nothing. I might just as well have been on another planet, I thought, as I looked from one pair of dark eyes to another. I had no idea if they had even heard me. Then I started to wonder if they understood English. Maybe I needed an interpreter.

"Would it be better if I had an interpreter?" I asked.

There was no change in expression. Neither took his eyes off me.

"Here's how I was thinking that you may be able to help me." I decided I might as well continue, but the next time, if I knew they were coming in, I'd have an interpreter here. "I was wondering if it would be possible for one of you, or one of your people, to advise me whenever your band shoots an animal. All I want to know is when and where. Then I won't have to spend another freezing night watching the site. Do you think that would be possible?"

I had resigned myself to the fact that I was not going to get an answer, but I waited, hoping for some sign of acknowledgement.

"I would also like to know if you are interested in any of the meat that I pick up from time to time?" I asked, thinking that this would be an excellent opportunity to have a legitimate source for disposing of seizures. At least I knew these people could and would use it.

"Sometimes meat is forfeited, and when that happens I have to give it away," I explained. "All I require is a signature to show where it has gone. And of course there are numerous roadkills in this area. If you're interested, I can see that you get them as well." I drew another blank, as there was no response to this offer either.

Then suddenly, without any warning and to my complete surprise, they both stood up, both at the same time, as if there was a hidden cue. They turned and walked out of the office. I raced around the desk and followed them to the front door.

"Good day, gentlemen," I called after them. "Thanks

for taking the time to come in," I mumbled as the door closed in my face. I turned to the steno. "Well, I certainly made a lasting impression on them," I commented.

"What did they say?" she asked.

"Nothing," I replied. "Not one single word. They never said hello, they never said goodbye. They walked in, they sat, they never took their eyes off me, then they got up and walked out. It was as simple as that."

"What're you going to do now?" she asked.

"Nothing," I replied helplessly. "I'll probably freeze my butt off the next time they shoot a moose, though. Oh well, it was worth a try. Nothing ventured, nothing gained. But you know, it would have been nice if they'd said something."

About a month later I was standing by the counter in the office when I noticed the smaller of the two men, one of my silent guests, crossing the street. To my surprise, he walked past my car, up the steps, and into my office.

"Good morning, sir," I greeted him with a big smile, sort of like we were old friends, and extended my hand in a gesture of friendship.

He didn't smile and he ignored my attempt to shake his hand. He just looked at me with those dark eyes and stood there for what seemed to be an eternity. Another one of those silent visits, I thought, but why? This time I hadn't asked for a meeting, nor was I expecting one.

"Please, come on in. Can I get you a coffee?" I extended my arm towards my office, indicating the way. He didn't move. He waited for awhile, then spoke.

"Some of my people will go to the lower Wildhay River — by the airstrip — they will shoot a cow moose," he said quietly.

I was so surprised, I stood there with my mouth open. Finally, I regained my senses enough to stutter, "I-I want to thank you very much for being so helpful. Your thoughtfulness will save me a lot of work and keep me from freezing."

We both stood there for a couple of minutes in silence, then I asked, "Would you have any idea when your people might go to the Wildhay to hunt?"

"Monday," was the one-word reply.

"I want to thank you again for all your help."

With that, he turned and walked out of the office. There was no hello, no goodbye, just a short, to-the-point message.

When I came into the office on Wednesday, there was a complaint on my desk. Someone reported a moose having been shot on the lower Wildhay River road, near the airstrip. My curiosity was killing me, and I immediately drove to the site. I could only smile when I found the spot where a cow moose lay, covered with snow. I was delighted as I signed off the complaint.

For the next three years I received many similar visits, each one short and sweet. I always knew in advance when his people would be going hunting. I knew the location and I even knew the date. What amazed me, though, was that I also knew the species and the sex of the animal. It certainly made life simple for me.

Providing meat to the camp was simple enough, but it was different. The first animal I obtained that could be given to them was a road-killed moose. When I drove into the camp, I got the same greeting I had received on my first visit. The only sign of life was the smoke drifting up from the chimneys. When no one appeared, I left the meat on a canvas by one of the tents and left. As I was driving away, I looked in the rear-view mirror. Several shadows emerged from the cover of the trees, moving towards the meat. I didn't go back.

The next time he came into the office, I advised him that I could leave the roadkills without a signature, but not any confiscated meat. He never responded. Again there was no way I could read his mind. But the information I had received earlier had been correct, and I knew he would never sign a piece of paper. This camp would get the roadkills.

The last winter that I was in Hinton, both men showed up at my office. In the past I had always invited them in and offered a coffee. They never accepted the offer. On this day they both walked past the counter and into my private office and sat down before I had extended the customary invitation. There was the usual long period of silence.

"I'm going to shoot a cow elk with the calf still inside," the smaller of the two said matter-of-factly.

"Okay," I replied. "The cows will start calving in about six weeks' time. When and where are you going to do this?"

"In about a month, but I don't know where yet."

"I would think that shooting a cow elk with an

177

unborn calf would be a matter of great importance," I commented, not really asking a question because I never expected an answer.

Another long silence. I looked from one to the other. Man, but the silence, the uncertainty, was nerve-racking. I knew in my heart they were going to get up and walk out any minute.

"I need the skin from the unborn calf," he finally replied.

"I see," I answered. "Maybe I could help you. If I can get you the skin from an unborn calf, could you use it?"

"I have to skin it myself," he informed me. "It has to be fresh."

He was talking, slowly and in his own good time. He had already said more on this day than he had said in all the time I knew him. This was a major breakthrough. I was afraid to say anything for fear that I would scare them off, but it was important to know if he could make use of a hide collected by someone other than himself.

"If I can get a fresh calf, would that be acceptable?" I asked cautiously. "I would bring it right to your camp." There was no answer. No yes. No no. Just silence.

"The hide has to be tanned in a special way," he finally replied.

"I understand," I answered, certain that he had finished speaking.

"I have to record everything that has happened to my people in the last one hundred years on the skin of an unborn elk. It is important that the spots are on the skin. Every one hundred years we do that, and this is the year I must do that."

I sat, waiting for more. No one spoke for several minutes. "That sounds very exciting," I replied, hoping that I wasn't interrupting again. "I'll bet it's a proud moment in your life to be able to record history for your people? I would like to be able to help you. Is there anything that I can do?"

Suddenly, they both stood up and left. There was never a hello, never a goodbye. They drifted in and out of my world like the wind.

There was a late April storm that year, and I received a call that several elk had been hit by a train in the Obed Hills east of Hinton. I raced to the scene by Ski-Doo as soon as I received the call. Parts and pieces of elk were scattered all over the right of way. What a mess, I thought, as I surveyed the carnage. But a pregnant cow had been killed. The carcass was still intact. I carefully opened her up and removed the perfectly formed unborn calf. I carefully wiped off the little body, the small white spots speckling the light-brown hide. I was very careful not to make a mark on the carcass. Although neither of my guests had told me that they would accept the calf, they had not rejected the offer either.

As quickly as I could, I headed straight for the camp. This visit to the camp was like all the others. There was fire in the stoves and smoke in the chimneys, but there were no people. There were never any people. Very carefully I took the calf and laid it on a tarp, and then left. Once more, in the rear-view mirror, I observed shadows emerge from the forest and move towards the offering.

Next morning I had a visitor. The smaller man was by himself when he entered the office.

"Good morning," I greeted him warmly. "Would you like to come in for a coffee?" I asked, extending my arm towards my office.

He stayed by the counter. "I skinned the calf," he informed me, displaying no emotion. "It is a good skin. I will tan it, then I will record the history of my people on it."

"I'm glad I was able to help you," I beamed happily. "I'm sure you will do a fine job. Your people will be very proud."

Like always, he turned and left.

In June of that same year I received confirmation from the Department that I would be transferred to Calgary. Shortly after receiving the letter, I met both men on the street. You could have knocked my socks off when the smaller man stopped.

"I have been told you are going to Calgary," he said. Other than in my office, it was the only time he had ever shown any sign of recognizing me, let alone stopping to talk.

"Yes. That's right, I'll be going to Calgary at the end of the month," I confirmed.

"You don't have to go," he stated. "I can arrange for you to stay. I will talk to the Premier."

"Th-the Premier, holy mackerel," I stammered, and I was thinking rapidly. This quiet, humble man moves in big circles — the Premier, he's at the top of the Powers-That-Be chain — and he's deadly serious.

"You have been good to work with," he said. "It would be good if you stayed."

Now it was my turn to stand there not saying anything. Those dark eyes were still just looking at me without blinking. They never changed and they never gave me a hint of what the man was thinking.

"No . . . no, it is you who has been good to work with. You are a man of your word. And . . . and thank you very much for your kind offer," I finally blurted out. "But the decision to go is mine. It's for personal reasons. I have to make this move. But I thank you very much for your concern."

"Remember, you don't have to go if you don't want to. I will speak for you. Let me know if you change your mind."

I felt sad, but at the same time I felt honoured. I could feel a tear welling up as he turned and walked away.

He never said goodbye, but then, he had never said hello.

ROBERT J. (BOB) ADAMS

Bob Adams was born in Turner Valley, Alberta in 1938. He grew up in the Edson area, in a log house, built by his father on a farm rich in swamp spruce, tamarack, willows and muskeg.

Bob, an avid outdoorsman, was one of the fortunate few who was able to live his boyhood dreams as he entered the workforce. In 1960, after a number of years with the Alberta Forest Service and Royal Canadian Mounted Police, he began a career with the Provincial Government as a Fish and Wildlife Officer. For the next 33 years, he found his homes to include Brooks, Strathmore, Hinton, Calgary, Peace River and Edmonton.

In 1993, after a full career in Enforcement, he retired from Fish and Wildlife and wrote his first book, The Stump Farm. Today, Bob resides in Edmonton, Alberta with his wife Martha where he continues to work on his writing.

GIVE A "ROBERT J. ADAMS" BOOK TO A FRIEND

Megamy Publishing Ltd.
Box 3507
Spruce Grove, AB   T7X 3A7

Send to:

Name:_____

Street:_____

City:_____

Province/   Postal/
State:_____ Zip Code:_____

Please send:

   "The Stump Farm"   @ $18.95 =_____

   "Beyond the Stump Farm"   @ $18.95 =_____

   "Horse Cop"   @ $18.95 =_____

   "Fish Cop"   @ $18.95 =_____

   "The Elephant's Trunk"   @ $18.95 =_____

   "The South Road"   @ $18.95 =_____

   "Skunks and Hound Dogs"   @ $18.95 =_____

   "In the Shadow of the Rockies" @ $18.95 =_____

   "Dynamite Hill"   @ $18.95 =_____

Shipping and handling per book @ $ 5.00 =_____

7% GST =_____

Total amount enclosed: _____

Make cheque or money order payable to:
Megamy Publishing Ltd.
Price subject to change without prior notice.
ORDERS OUTSIDE OF CANADA must be paid in U.S. funds by
cheque or money order drawn on U.S. or Canadian Bank.
Sorry no C.O.D.'s.